Key to the identification of British centipedes

By A.D. Barber

Rathgar, Exeter Road, Ivybridge, Devon PL21 0BD

BRINGING
ENVIRONMENTAL
UNDERSTANDING TO ALL

First Edition 2008
© FSC 2008
ISBN 978 1 85153 242 1
Occasional Publication 130

ACKNOWLEDGEMENTS

Thanks to the late Ted Eason whose *Centipedes of the British Isles* was the start of a renewed interest in chilopods in this country and for information, advice and encouragement over many years both to myself and to others and for allowing the use of his diagrams.

Also to John Lewis and to the late Gordon Blower, prime movers in the establishment of the British Myriapod Group (now the British Myriapod and Isopod Group), for help and support, to Colin Fairhurst who initiated the recording schemes for myriapods, to Andy Keay and Dick Jones for many helpful comments on draft keys and the latter also for valuable drawings.

To Prof. Alessandro Minelli and Dr. Lucio Bonato for advice on nomenclature and to the latter for comments on the geophilomorph key and for examining specimens of *Tygarrup* and *Mecistocephalus*.

And to all contributors to the myriapod recording schemes who contributed so much to an increased knowledge of our centipedes and millipedes.

Most of the diagrams used in this key are from E.H. Eason *Centipedes of the British Isles*, Warne, 1964 with others from articles in the Bulletin of the British Myriapod Group and elsewhere.

Colour plates are by Dick Jones, Paul Richards and the author.

CONTENTS

INTRODUCTION

Centipedes are some of the commonest larger arthropods found in gardens, waste ground, woodland, grassland and moorland; several species are more or less exclusively found on the sea shore, often intertidally. Centipedes are immediately recognisable by their large number of legs (15 or more pairs) borne one pair per segment (Fig. 1a) and by a pair of poison claws immediately under the head. The only animals they could possibly be confused with are Symphyla which are whitish and with only 11 or 12 pairs of legs usually about 4 mm or so long (Fig. 1b) and some of the 'flat-backed' millipedes such as *Polydesmus* which have two pairs of legs per segment (Fig. 1c). Neither of these has poison claws.

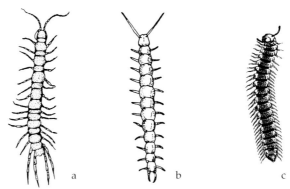

Fig. 1. A centipede (a), with members of the only other taxa that could possibly be mistaken for one – a symphylan (b) and the millipede *Polydesmus denticulatus* (c).
[a and b from Tilling (1987), c from Koch (1863).]

General structure

The body of a centipede comprises: a head bearing mouthparts, antennae, and, in some types, eyes; a segment bearing the poison claws (forcipular segment); a series of leg-bearing trunk segments; and then terminal segments with genitalia.

There are four orders of centipede recorded from the British Isles, the long, worm-like geophilomorphs (earth centipedes) with 35 or more pairs of legs; scolopendromorphs which are brownish species with 21 pairs; lithobiomorphs (stone centipedes) with 15 pairs of legs and scutigeromorphs (house centipedes) which also have fifteen leg pairs but these are very elongate and the animals are quite spider-like.

These four orders all have a common basic structure but differ considerably from one to another and reference to some of these differences will be made in this account. Because of their differences, different characteristics are used in classification and identification and an account of aspects of these is given with the account of each order.

The dorsal shield of the head is convex and continuous anteriorly with a ventral flap, the clypeus (Fig. 4). The are also lateral flaps, pleurites, continuous with the head shield (Fig. 2). At the anterior end there are two antennae, each made up of a number of articles (segments), different for each order. At the sides there may be simple eyes (ocelli) not comparable with the compound eye of insects except in scutigeromorphs where there are true compound eyes. Geophilomorphs and British scolopendromorphs are blind.

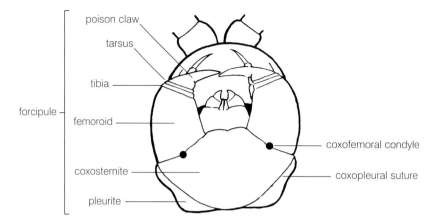

Fig. 2. Diagram of the ventral side of a centipede's head showing the forcipules (from Eason 1964).

Underneath the head the most obvious structures are the so-called poison claws or forcipules, a pair of highly modified legs (Fig. 2). In this account the entire pair of modified legs is referred to as the forcipules, restricting the term poison claws for their terminal parts with the actual claw. The base of the forcipules is termed the coxosternite (forcipular coxosternite) and this is a very solid structure, narrower posteriorly. The front edge of this coxosternite may bear teeth or other structures. The remainder of the forcipule comprises a large femoroid, smaller tibia and tarsus and the poison claw itself which has the duct from a poison gland opening at its tip. The mouthparts (maxillae; mandibles) lie above the forcipules (i.e. underneath them when examining an animal from the underside, see Figs 3 and 4). Below these, when viewed from above is the labrum, an extension of the clypeus, sometimes useful in identification (Fig. 4).

The poison is used in the capture of the animal's prey but in only the very largest of British specimens is the claw strong enough to penetrate human skin (some of the large *Cryptops* or *Lithobius*) and the effect is noticeable but generally insignificant. In geophilomorphs the claw may bear a more or less prominent basal node (tooth) (Fig. 43) and the inner surface of the claw (concavity) may have various crenulations or incisures (Fig. 46).

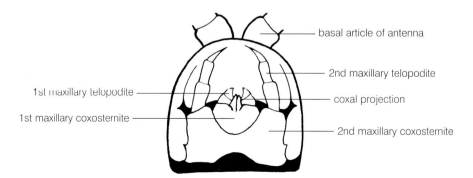

Fig. 3. Diagram of the ventral side of the head with the forcipules removed showing the maxillae (from Eason 1964).

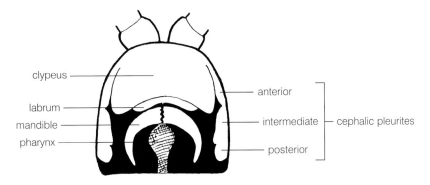

Fig. 4. Diagram of the ventral side of the head with forcipules and maxillae removed (from Eason 1964).

Body segments of centipedes, like those of insects, are confined within a series of chitinous plates. Dorsally there is a tergite and ventrally a sternite both of which may be divided. Laterally there are various pleurites (Fig. 5). The appearance of the tergite of the forcipular segment and those of the trunk segments are useful in identification in some species. In geophilomorphs the sternites may bear various fossae (pits), pegs and pore areas. These latter comprise the opening of a number of small glands and the shape and general appearance of these is of value in identification.

The legs comprise a basal coxa and a series of articles (segments): trochanter, prefemur, femur, tibia, tarsus, metatarsus and claw (Fig. 5). These may bear various spines or other structures and there may be one or more accessory claws. When an animal such as *Lithobius* is described as having a double claw on the last legs, this refers to a relatively large main claw and a smaller accessory claw. The first pair of legs may be relatively small compared with subsequent ones and the last pair are often markedly different. In geophilomorphs the coxae of the last pair of legs bear various numbers of coxal pores, the appearance of which is valuable in identification, in *Cryptops* (scolopendromorph) there are numerous pores on the coxae (cribriform area) and in lithobiomorphs a row of ventral pores on the coxae of each of the last four pairs of legs.

The terminal segments bear the genitalia and it is often helpful to be able to sex lithobiomorphs and geophilomorphs (described for each of these orders) as differences in other aspects of the sexes such as segment number, appearance of last legs, secondary structures on the legs, etc. may be helpful in identification. The gonopods themselves are generally of limited value in separating species although the characteristics of the female gonopod spurs and claw in lithobiomorphs can sometimes be very useful.

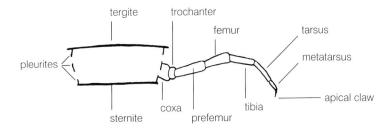

Fig. 5. Diagram of a transverse section through a trunk segment and one appendage (from Eason 1964).

Development

Centipedes go through a series of instars (stages) after hatching and characteristics of the adult animal gradually develop at each moult (ecdysis). Geophilomorphs hatch with the adult number of leg pairs but the number of coxal pores and the characteristics of other features are reduced. As they mature various characters develop more fully but the segment number remains the same and this segment number (number of pairs of legs) is a valuable aid in identification. In *Cryptops* there is also a complete number of segments at birth but progressive development of some definitive structures such as the tibial and tarsal combs making them less satisfactory for discrimination between species in very young animals.

In lithobiomorphs and scutigeromorphs the earliest stages have fewer leg pairs than adults and behind these are limb buds from which legs develop with each moult until the post larval stages with the complete number of legs (15 pairs) are reached.

Immediately after their moult and before full pigmentation develops, centipedes may differ in colour from normal and unusual coloured animals such as violet *Lithobius* may be seen. Occasional abnormally coloured geophilomorphs occur such as 'fluorescent' *Geophilus osquidatum*. This may possibly be due to a parasitic infection.

COLLECTION AND IDENTIFICATION

Certain species can be identified in the field with or without a hand lens but it is always a good idea to collect voucher specimens of even common animals unless, like *Lithobius variegatus* they are completely unmistakable. Centipedes are one of several groups of invertebrates for which it is usually necessary to collect, kill and preserve specimens (best done by dropping directly into 70% alcohol (IMS) to be sure of their identity). 95% of large brown lithobiids will be *Lithobius forficatus* (except in parts of SW England or the Channel Islands for instance) but it is always as well to check as both *L. peregrinus*, *L. piceus* and *L. pilicornis* look rather similar. Small animals will almost always need to be examined closely.

There is no single way to collect these animals; different workers using different techniques may find unusual species. However using a pair of forceps to pick them up and subsequently dropping into 70% alcohol will usually be the final stage. Hand sorting under logs and stones and in leaf litter, sieving, pitfall traps, Tullgren extraction, cracking open rock crevices, etc. may all yield results but season, location, weather all play their part along with chance in finding species. Some people when hand sorting litter collect a handful of litter containing the animal and then sort it out on a white tray or old piece of plastic sheet.

Specimens should be stored in glass tubes in 70% alcohol to which a small amount of glycerol (about 5%) may be added. Labels should be written in alcohol resistant ink (or pencil) on spirit proof paper (e.g. computer/photocopier paper) and put inside the tube along with any detached legs or other structures. It is important to record locality, date and preferably habitat. Straightening freshly killed animals out (some people use drinking straws for geophilomorphs) is useful before they become hard. It is also a good idea to do this with the last legs of *Cryptops*. Care should be taken with collections to prevent any drying out of preserved animals.

Ideally a low power binocular microscope is used to examine specimens but a high power conventional microscope may be used for looking at detail or small specimens. Using a suitable bright light shone down from above on to the specimen, immersed in alcohol and viewed at x20 under the binocular microscope is a good starting point for examination. The use of dark or light background depends on the circumstances as does the angle of the light. Small glass beads or cotton wool are often valuable for orientating specimens other than on their dorsal or ventral surface. Fine forceps and needles are probably the only instruments required. Some features, such as sternal pores or the sculpturing on *Cryptops* are best seen if the animal is removed from spirit and allowed to dry slightly before examination but on no account allow it to become dry and brittle.

To see certain features such as the coxal pores of *Stenotaenia linearis* it may be useful to clear the animal in Hoyer's mountant or use 50% lactic acid with gentle warming (N.B. lactic acid is an irritant; eye or skin contact may cause severe burns; gloves and safety glasses should be worn). This *may* also allow certain features such as the labrum to be seen without dissection. There are some problems with Hoyer's mountant; it is unsuitable for permanent mounts and difficulty may be experienced in returning specimens to alcohol. An alternative is the use of ethylene glycol for temporary mounts, especially of geophilomorphs (see Pereira, 2000). If animals are dissected then mouthparts, etc. should be stored in a small tube or mounted on a slide and carefully labelled.

With experience, it may possible to make identification of certain species with distinctive features whilst they are still alive using a good hand lens or a low power stereomicroscope. For this purpose, each animal may be placed in a transparent cellophane/plastic envelope of the type favoured by some stamp and postcard dealers and then carefully held flat for examination. However, the technique is not universally applicable and, in any case, it is desirable to retain voucher specimens of any unusual species.

The keys are designed to be as user-friendly as possible but obviously include terms that may be unfamiliar. These are generally illustrated in the key and/or glossary.

Always check the identification against the species notes – and assume that the animal you are looking at is most likely to be a common species unless there are clear features that tell you otherwise. It is also helpful to note the distribution of the species. Some unusual species such as *Lithobius muticus* and *L. tricuspis* have been recorded from sites outside their 'normal' range but it is always helpful to check. It is likely that further species may be found in Britain – since the publication of E.H. Eason's classic *Centipedes of the British Isles* in 1964 some 9 further species have been recorded from outdoor locations in England or Scotland. If you think that you do have something new then do please contact an expert e.g. via the British Myriapod & Isopod Group's website (BMIG.org.uk).

THE CENTIPEDE RECORDING SCHEME

This has been in operation since the 1970s as part of the work of the British Myriapod & Isopod Group and in association with the UK Biological Records Centre. It offers advice, identifications/verifications, etc. as well as collecting records on habitat and distribution. There was a Provisional Atlas in 1988 (Barber and Keay).

The BMIG publishes a twice yearly Newsletter and, approximately annually, a more formal Bulletin and arranges an annual field meeting somewhere in the UK.

Habitats for centipedes

Gardens, urban waste sites, town parks, etc.

Often a source of unusual species. The characteristics of synanthropic habitats often favour species whose normal occurrence would be from more southerly sites. Look under rubbish, stones, wood, moss, etc. for species such as *Stigmatogaster subterranea*, *Schendyla dentata*, *Henia brevis*, *Geophilus electricus*, *Geophilus carpophagus*, *Cryptops* spp., *Lithobius forficatus*, *Lithobius melanops*, *Lithobius microps*, etc.

Woodland

Various types of woodland offer a wide variety of species. This is a typical habitat for *Stigmatogaster subterranea* (in the South West), *Strigamia* spp., *Geophilus easoni*, *Geophilus truncorum* (under bark and in leaf litter), *Lithobius variegatus*, *Lithobius macilentus*, *Lithobius muticus*, *Lithobius crassipes*, *Lithobius curtipes*, etc.

Grassland

Not always easy to sample but digging in turf, trapping or extraction methods can yield a variety of species such as *Geophilus truncorum*, *Lithobius variegatus*, *Lithobius forficatus*, *Lithobius calcaratus*, *Lithobius crassipes*, etc.

Arable

Often difficult to locate suitable microsites but can yield various species such as *Geophilus flavus*, *Lithobius forficatus*, *Lithobius crassipes*, *Lithobius microps*, etc.

Heath, upland moor

Typical species include *Geophilus easoni*, *Geophilus truncorum*, *Lithobius variegatus*, *Lithobius borealis* or *Lithobius crassipes* (depending on region), *Lithobius calcaratus*.

Maritime

Littoral species are *Hydroschendyla submarina*, *Schendyla peyerimhoffi*, *Geophilus gracilis* and *Strigamia maritima*. *Lithobius melanops*, *Geophilus flavus* and *Lithobius forficatus* are also commonly found above the tide line and the only outdoor records for *Lithobius lapidicola* are from maritime locations. Search in shingle, strand line debris, under stones on muddy, sandy and rocky shores, in rock crevices.

Glasshouses

A number of unusual species have been recorded from heated greenhouses whilst unheated ones might yield *Lithobius forficatus*, *Lithobius melanops*, *Crytops hortensis* and *Geophilus carpophagus* amongst other types.

SYSTEMATIC LIST OF BRITISH CENTIPEDE SPECIES

Names as in 'Chilobase' database (chilobase.bio.unipd.it).

* Species recorded from inside buildings or greenhouses only (in mainland Britain).

† Species of doubtful status in the British Isles.

Class CHILOPODA
  Order GEOPHILOMORPHA

  Family MECISTOCEPHALIDAE

    Dicellophilus carniolensis (C. Koch, 1847) *
    Tygarrup javanicus (Attems, 1907) *
    Mecistocephalus guildingii Newport, 1843 *

  Family HIMANTARIIDAE

    Stigmatogaster subterranea (Shaw, 1789)
      (*Haplophilus subterraneus* (Shaw, 1789))
    Stigmatogaster souletina (Brolemann, 1907)
      (*Nesoporogaster souletina brevior* Eason, 1962)

  Family SCHENDYLIDAE

    Hydroschendyla submarina (Grube, 1869)
    Schendyla nemorensis (C.L. Koch, 1837)
    Schendyla peyerimhoffi Brolemann & Ribaut, 1911
    Schendyla carniolensis Verhoeff, 1902 †
      (*Schendyla zonalis* Brolemann & Ribaut, 1911)
    Schendyla monoeci Brolemann, 1904 *
      (*Brachyschendyla monoeci* (Brolemann, 1904))
    Schendyla dentata (Brolemann & Ribaut, 1911)
      (*Brachyschendyla dentata* (Brolemann & Ribaut, 1911))

  Family DIGNATHODONTIDAE

    Henia vesuviana (Newport, 1844)
      (*Chaetechelyne vesuviana* (Newport, 1844))
    Henia brevis Silvestri 1896
      (*Chaetechelyne montana oblongocribellata* Verhoeff, 1898)

  Family LINTOTAENIIDAE

    Strigamia crassipes (C.L. Koch, 1835)
    Strigamia acuminata (Leach, 1814)
    Strigamia maritima (Leach, 1817)

Family GEOPHILIDAE

Pachymerium ferrugineum (C.L. Koch, 1835)
Nothogeophilus turki Lewis, Jones & Keay, 1988
Stenotaenia linearis (C.L. Koch, 1835)
    (*Clinopodes linearis* (C.L. Koch, 1835))
Geophilus carpophagus Leach, 1814
Geophilus easoni Arthur et al., 2001
Geophilus electricus (Linné, 1758)
Geophilus osquidatum Brolemann, 1909
Geophilus gracilis Meinert, 1870
    (*Geophilus fucorum seurati* Brolemann, 1924)
Geophilus pusillifrater Verhoeff, 1898
Geophilus insculptus Attems, 1895
    (*Geophilus alpinus* Meinert, 1870)
Geophilus proximus C.L. Koch, 1847
Geophilus flavus (De Geer, 1778)
    (*Necrophloeophagus longicornis* (Leach, 1814))
Geophilus truncorum Bergsoë & Meinert, 1886
    (*Brachygeophilus truncorum* (Bergsoë & Meinert, 1886))
Eurygeophilus pinguis (Brolemann, 1898)
    (*Chalandea pinguis* (Brolemann, 1898))
Arenophilus peregrinus Jones, 1989

Order SCOLOPENDROMORPHA

Family SCOLOPENDRIDAE

Scolopendra species ('giant centipedes') are occasionally imported accidentally with fruit, etc.

Family CRYPTOPSIDAE

Cryptops anomalans Newport, 1844
Cryptops hortensis (Donovan, 1810)
Cryptops parisi Brolemann, 1920
Cryptops doriae Pocock, 1891 *

Order LITHOBIOMORPHA

Family LITHOBIIDAE

Lithobius variegatus Leach, 1813
Lithobius peregrinus Latzel, 1880
Lithobius forficatus (Linné, 1758)
Lithobius piceus L. Koch, 1862
　　　(*Lithobius quadridentatus* Menge, 1851)
Lithobius melanops Newport, 1845
Lithobius macilentus L. Koch, 1862
　　　(*Lithobius aulacopus* Latzel, 1880)
Lithobius tricuspis Meinert, 1872
Lithobius agilis C.L. Koch, 1847 †
Lithobius tenebrosus Meinert, 1872
　　　(*Lithobius nigrifrons* Latzel & Haase, 1880)
Lithobius erythrocephalus C.L. Koch, 1847 †
Lithobius borealis Meinert, 1868
　　　(*Lithobius lapidicola* Latzel, 1880)
Lithobius lapidicola Meinert, 1872
　　　(*Lithobius pusillus* Latzel, 1880)
Lithobius pilicornis Newport, 1844
Lithobius calcaratus C.L. Koch, 1844
Lithobius muticus C.L. Koch, 1862
Lithobius lucifugus L. Koch, 1862
Lithobius crassipes L. Koch, 1862
Lithobius curtipes C.L. Koch, 1847
Lithobius microps Meinert, 1868
　　　(*Lithobius duboscqui* Brolemann, 1896)

Family HENICOPIDAE

Lamyctes caeculus (Brolemann, 1899) *
　　　(*Lamyctinus coeculus* (Brolemann, 1899))
Lamyctes emarginatus (Newport, 1844)
　　　(*Lamyctes fulvicornis* Meinert, 1868)

Order SCUTIGEROMORPHA

Family SCUTIGERIDAE

Scutigera coleoptrata (Linné, 1758) *

Suggested English names for centipedes

Like many groups of invertebrates, centipedes in general do not have vernacular names although geophilomorphs have been called at various times 'wireworms' or 'wire centipedes' referring to their shape or 'glow-worms' relating to luminescence in some species. *Scutigera coleoptrata*, commonly found in buildings in many parts of the world is very frequently referred to as the 'house centipede'. The large scolopendromorphs from the tropics are usually called 'giant centipedes'.

With these exceptions, there are no accepted English names. However there has been pressure to create such names and the list given results from discussions amongst members of the British Myriapod and Isopod Group. The group does not recommend their use in general since they feel that it will likely lead to confusion. However, in some circumstances, notably in relation to certain conservation issues, it may be helpful to have an English name for a particular species. In this case, to avoid any possible confusion, the scientific (Latin) name should be given as well. Although scientific names do change from time to time there is a recognised procedure and publication of such changes and synonyms are currently checkable on the web-site 'Chilobase' (chilobase.bio.unipd.it).

Geophilomorpha	**Earth centipedes**
Arenophilus peregrinus	Least shore centipede
Dicellophilus carniolensis	Bagnall's hot-house centipede
Eurygeophilus pinguis	Devonshire paradox/Cut-short centipede
Geophilus carpophagus	Luminous centipede
Geophilus easoni	Eason's geophilus
Geophilus electricus	Linneaus' centipede
Geophilus flavus	Long-horned geophilus
Geophilus gracilis	Beach geophilus
Geophilus insculptus	Common geophilus
Geophilus osquidatum	Western geophilus
Geophilus proximus	Northern geophilus
Geophilus pusillifrater	Scarce geophilus
Geophilus truncorum	Small geophilus
Henia brevis	Southern garden centipede
Henia vesuviana	White-striped centipede
Hydroschendyla submarina	Sea-shore schendylid
Mecistocephalus guildingii	Larger hot-house centipede
Nothogeophilus turki	Turk's geophilid

Pachymerium ferrugineum	Red-headed centipede
Schendyla dentata	Toothed schendyla
Schendyla monoeci	Turk's greenhouse schendyla
Schendyla nemorensis	Common schendyla
Schendyla peyerimhoffi	Lesser shore schendyla
Stenotaenia linearis	Larger urban geophilus
Stigmatogaster souletina	Cornish yellow centipede
Stigmatogaster subterranea	Western yellow centipede
Strigamia acuminata	Shorter red centipede
Strigamia crassipes	Longer red centipede
Strigamia maritima	Maritime centipede
Tygarrup javanicus	Smaller hot-house centipede

Scolopendromorpha   **Cryptopid centipedes**

Cryptops anomalans	Greater cryptops
Cryptops hortensis	Common cryptops
Cryptops parisi	Paris cryptops

Lithobiomorpha   **Stone centipedes**

Lamyctes caeculus	Glasshouse lamyctes
Lamyctes emarginatus	One-eyed centipede
Lithobius borealis	Western lithobius
Lithobius calcaratus	Black lithobius
Lithobius crassipes	Thick-legged lithobius
Lithobius curtipes	Curling lithobius
Lithobius forficatus	Common lithobius
Lithobius lapidicola	Sandy lithobius
Lithobius lucifugus	Montane lithobius
Lithobius macilentus	Virgin lithobius
Lithobius melanops	Garden lithobius
Lithobius microps	Least lithobius
Lithobius muticus	Broad-headed lithobius
Lithobius peregrinus	Wandering lithobius

Lithobius piceus	Long-horned lithobius
Lithobius pilicornis	Greater lithobius
Lithobius tenebrosus	Scarce lithobius
Lithobius tricuspis	Three-spined lithobius
Lithobius variegatus	Variegated centipede/variegated lithobius

---

Scutigeromorpha

| *Scutigera coleoptrata* | House centipede |

KEY TO THE FOUR ORDERS OF CENTIPEDES RECORDED FROM BRITAIN

1   Elongate, worm-like species with 35 to 101 pairs of legs. No ocelli (Fig. 6) .... GEOPHILOMORPHA (p. 14)

-      Active, short bodied species with 15 or 21 pairs of legs, ocelli may be present 2

Fig. 6

2 (1) Light reddish brown species with 21 pairs of legs and no ocelli in British species (Fig. 7) .... SCOLOPENDROMORPHA (p. 48)

-      15 pairs of relatively long legs, ocelli usually present 3

Fig. 7

3 (2) Very elongate legs with up to 500 or more apparent segments in last pair, only seven tergites visible on trunk, dull violet with violet bands, normally found indoors, outdoors in Jersey (Fig. 8) .... SCUTIGEROMORPHA (p. 83)

Fig. 8

-      Legs with seven or so segments, relatively less elongate, 15 trunk tergites visible, alternating in size, light brown (with striations), chestnut brown or almost black, outdoors or indoors (Fig. 9) .... LITHOBIOMORPHA (p. 55)

Fig. 9

Geophilomorpha

These are the so called 'earth centipedes', elongate forms with from 35 to 101 pairs of legs in British species that have also sometimes been called 'wire centipedes' or 'wireworms' (not to be confused with the insect pest of that name). The number of leg bearing segments does not change during the life of a geophilomorph (unlike the situation in millipedes) and is a very useful character in identification. These centipedes appear rather more sluggish than the other centipede groups and are commonly found burrowing in soil, a habit for which their body design is appropriate. Some species are described as luminescent such as *Geophilus carpophagus* (s.l.), *Stigmatogaster subterranea* and *Strigamia crassipes*.

Unlike insects, the upper surface of each body segment is not always covered by a single tergite (plate). There is often a small pretergite followed by a larger metatergite (Fig. 10). Similarly the underside bears presternites and metasternites whilst the sides of the body are protected by various pleurites.

When identifying geophilomorphs, look especially for the leg number, shape of the head and forcipular tergite (Fig. 10), appearance of the coxae of the last legs and distinctive fossae (pits), areas of pores (sternal pore groups) and other structures on trunk sternites. Although colour, especially in the yellowish and whitish forms is not a good identification feature, the three *Strigamia* species, *Hydroschendyla submarina* and *Geophilus easoni* are all more or less distinctly reddish brown.

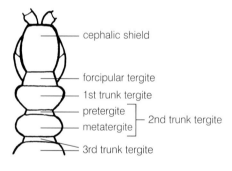

Fig. 10. Dorsal aspect of head and anterior tergites.

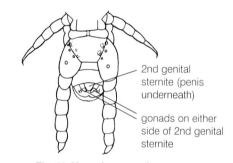

Fig. 11. Ventral aspect of posterior extremity of ♂ *Geophilus insculptus*.

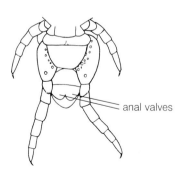

Fig. 12. Ventral aspect of posterior extremity of ♀ *Geophilus insculptus*.

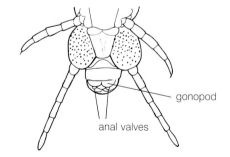

Fig. 13. Ventral aspect of posterior extremity of ♀ *Stigmatogaster subterranea*.

It is often helpful to check the sex of geophilomorphs and this may be done by examination of the ventral aspect of the terminal segments. In males there are a pair of distinct gonopods, located on either side of a central genital projection (Fig. 11) whilst in females there is either a pair of wide appendages or a short lamina (Figs 12 and 13). Obviously this is only possible in mature animals. In many species there is sexual dimorphism with males having much swollen last legs compared to the more slender ones of females.

Two means of identification are provided; a traditional dichotomous key (below), followed by a tabular key (p. 28) summarising the useful information. Both include all the geophilomorphs currently known from the British Isles (excluding the doubtful *Schendyla carniolensis*). Immature specimens may be difficult in some cases; some immature *Geophilus* species have 0, 1 or 2 coxal pores on their last legs in their early stages. An additional option has been included at various points in the key to allow for specimens with 2 or fewer pores on each side. In both *Geophilus truncorum* and the schendylids (which have two coxal pores in the adult stage) immatures may be seen with only one pore on each side and this is also the case with several other species. In certain species the earliest stage may have no coxal pores.

Key to British Geophilomorpha

1   Coxal pores distributed over the entire surface or at least most of the ventral (lower) surface of the coxae (basal segment) of the last legs (Fig. 14) 2

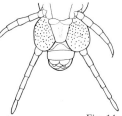

Fig. 14

-    Coxal pores of the last legs concentrated along the edge of the adjacent metasternite (Fig. 15) or opening into pits adjacent to it (Fig. 16) 10

NOTE: The coxal pores may be easier to see with a dark background and/or when the surface of the specimen has been allowed to dry out to a small extent (but not so much as to allow air to enter the body of the animal).

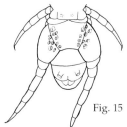

Fig. 15

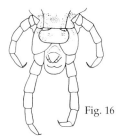

Fig. 16

2 (1) Coxal pores of last legs small and very numerous and distributed over both the dorsal (upper) and ventral (lower) surfaces (Fig. 17) 3

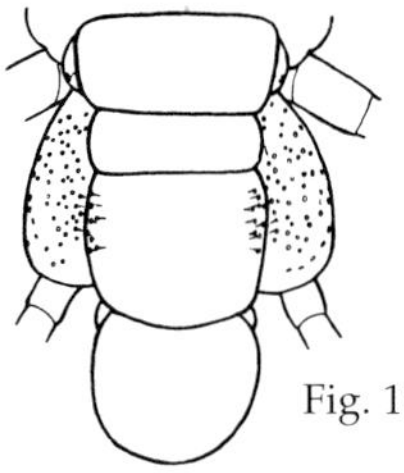

Fig. 17

- Coxal pores of last legs less numerous (Fig. 18) and distributed over the ventral surface only. Poison claw always with a well developed basal node or tooth (Fig. 19) 8

  NOTE: Fig. 18 shows a male *Strigamia crassipes* with much swollen terminal legs.

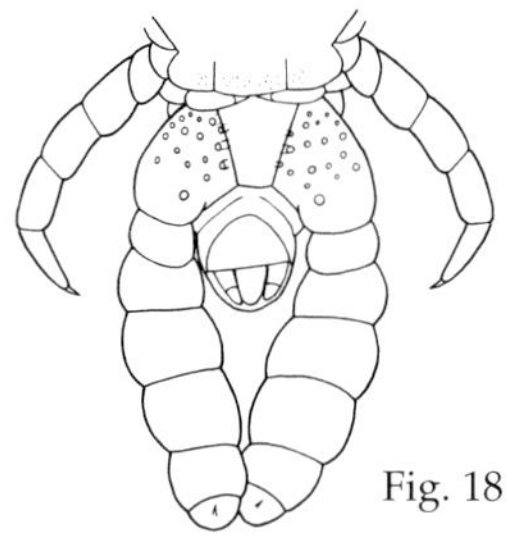

Fig. 18

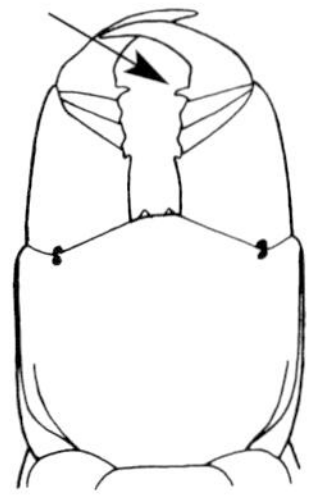

Fig. 19

3 (2) Head broader than long (Fig. 20). With more than 73 pairs of legs, generally yellowish in colour 4

  NOTE: Widespread, especially in SW, often in urban areas elsewhere.

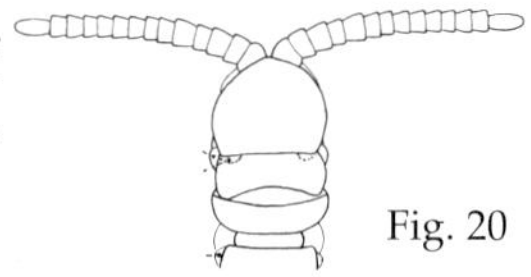

Fig. 20

- Head longer than broad (Fig. 21), less than 73 pairs of legs 5

  NOTE: Animals keying out here are either the hothouse species *Dicellophilus carniolensis*, *Mecistocephalus* sp. and *Tygarrup javanicus* or *Pachymerium ferrugineum* which has been found in Britain on only a few occasions in coastal shingle.

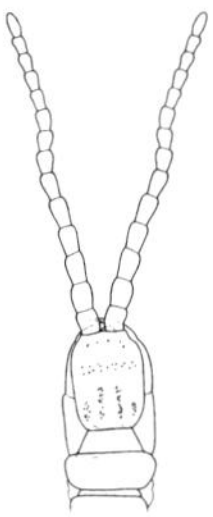

Fig. 21

4 (3) With 91 or more pairs of legs. Large transverse oval fossae (pits) on the sternites between approximately S40 and S49 (Fig. 22) .... *Stigmatogaster souletina* (p. 44)

NOTES:

S40, S49, etc. are the numbers of the trunk (body) sternites counted from the front end.

Rare species known from two Cornish sites.

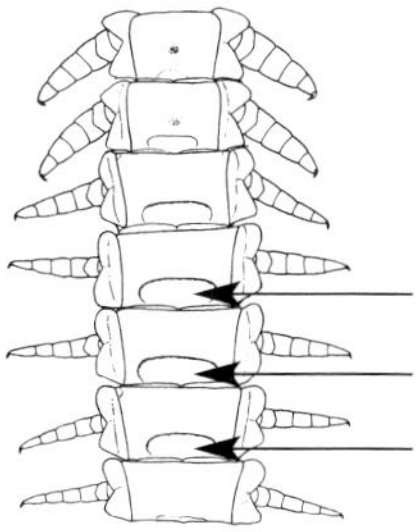

- With 73-85 pairs of legs and lacking large transverse sternal fossae .... *Stigmatogaster subterranea* (p. 44)

NOTES:

Formerly known as *Haplophilus subterraneus*.

Widespread in South and West, often synanthropic elsewhere.

Fig. 22

5 (3) With terminal claws on last pair of legs. Poison claw with smooth concavity (inner surface) and a prominent basal node (Fig. 23) .... *Pachymerium ferrugineum* (p. 40)

NOTE: Found in Britain on only a few occasions in coastal shingle.

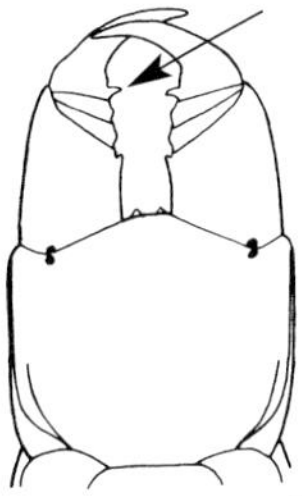

Fig. 23

- Without terminal claws on last legs, head much longer than wide and with a distinctly narrow and trapezoidal forcipular tergite (Fig. 24) 6

NOTE: Hothouse species.

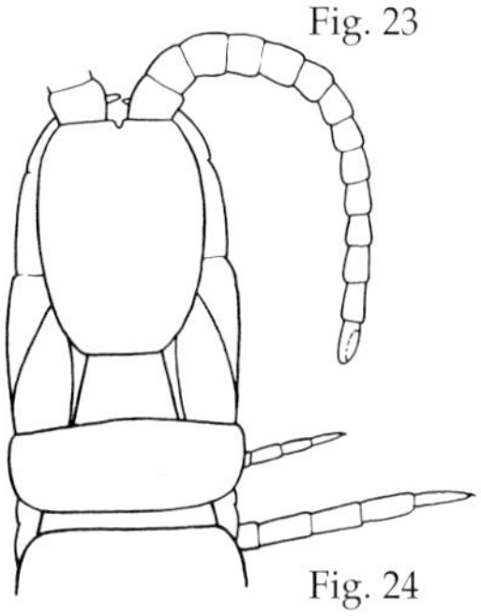

Fig. 24

6 (5) One large pore in the centre of a mass of small ones on the ventral surface of the last coxae (Fig. 25). 43 pairs of legs .... *Dicellophilus carniolensis* (p. 30)

- Pores on the ventral surface of the last coxae more or less uniformly small although the two innermost may be larger than the others. 45 or 49 pairs of legs 7

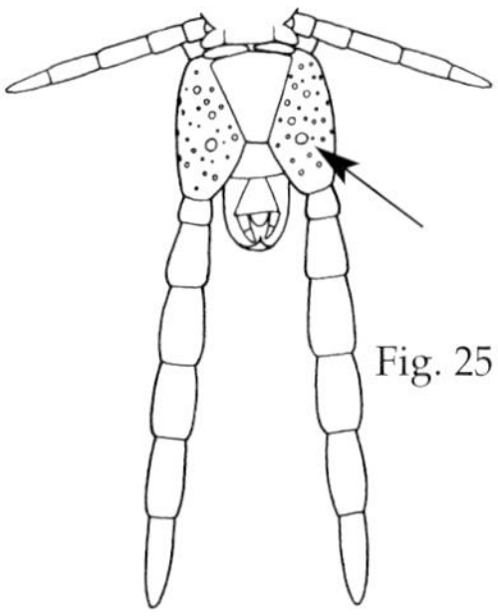

Fig. 25

7 (6) Relatively large species (up to 4 cm or more), 49 pairs of legs .... *Mecistocephalus guildingii* (p. 39)

- Smaller species (up to 2 cm), 45 pairs of legs .... *Tygarrup javanicus* (p. 47)

8 (2) With 37-41 pairs of legs. Sternites without a deep median cleft but with a shallow gutter (Fig. 26) .... *Strigamia acuminata* (p. 45)

NOTES:
Gutter may be best seen with slightly oblique light and some careful drying off.
Widespread terrestrial species.

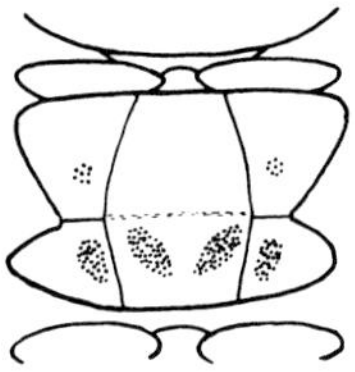

Fig. 26

-       With 47 or more pairs of legs 9

9 (8) The pleurites of last trunk segment separate from the adjacent pretergite (Fig. 27). Sternites do not have a deep cleft but a shallow circular depression. 47-51 pairs of legs .... *Strigamia maritima* (p. 46)

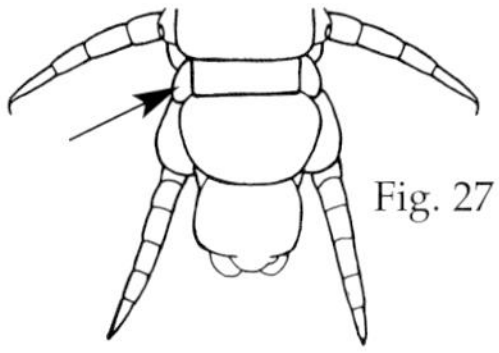

NOTE: Littoral species, widespread around the British Isles, occurring in shingle, under stones, etc. including estuarine sites. Often very abundant.

Fig. 27

-       The pleurites of the last trunk segment are fused to the pretergite. Sternites with a distinct deep longitudinal cleft (Fig. 28). 49-53 pairs of legs .... *Strigamia crassipes* (p. 45)

NOTES:
Sternite depression and cleft may be best seen with slightly oblique light and some careful drying off.

Widespread terrestrial species.

Immature *Strigamia* species have fewer coxal pores on the last legs but the tooth at the base of the poison claw is still relatively large making recognition fairly easy.

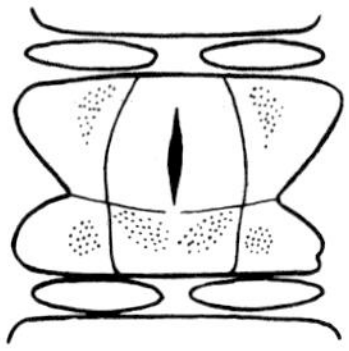

Fig. 28

10 (1) Head broader than long (Fig. 29). Forcipular tergite much the same breadth anteriorly as posteriorly, with strongly convex shoulders 11

Fig. 29

-       Head longer than broad (Fig. 30). Forcipular tergite broader posteriorly than anteriorly (trapezoidal), with more or less straight lateral borders 12

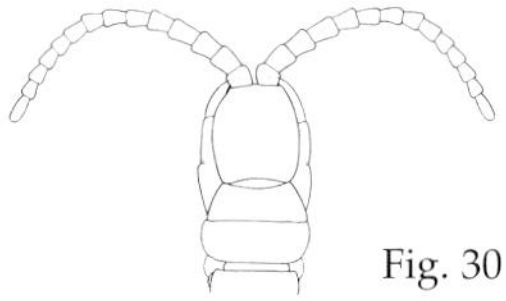

Fig. 30

11 (10) 61-75 pairs of legs. Large, stout species with more or less circular sternal pore groups (Fig. 31). Dorsal surface usually greenish-grey with narrow longitudinal white line .... *Henia vesuviana* (p. 38)

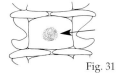

Fig. 31

NOTE: Southern species; coastal or inland usually in synanthropic sites.

- 53-57 pairs of legs. Small, pale species with elliptical/rectangular sternal pore groups (Fig. 32) .... *Henia brevis* (p. 37)

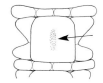

Fig. 32

NOTE: Southern, usually synanthropic.

12 (10) Sternal pore groups distinct on anterior segments (Fig. 33). Coxal pores on last legs open into pits adjacent to the metasternite (Fig. 34). 63-79 pairs of legs .... *Stenotaenia linearis* (p. 43)

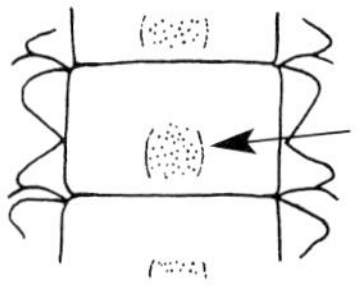

Fig. 33

NOTES:

The coxal pores opening into pits are often not very clear and the animal may appear to not have any pores at all at first. Examination of live animals against the light (e.g. whilst held in a transparent envelope) or clearing of preserved specimens (see page 5) may be helpful.

The sternal pore areas are more or less round and fairly clearly seen.

Generally synanthropic, southern Britain, widespread in the London area.

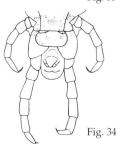

Fig. 34

- Sternal pores either absent or relatively indistinct (Fig. 35) when seen by direct illumination. Coxal pores of last legs open directly onto the surface (Fig. 36) 13

NOTE: Urban and rural sites throughout Britain.

Fig. 35

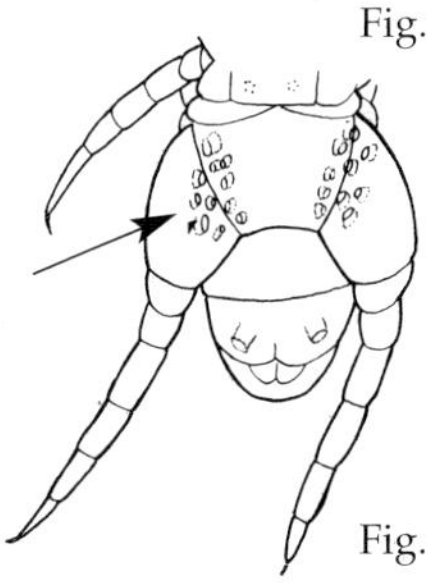

Fig. 36

13 (12) 1 or 0 coxal pores on last legs (Fig. 37) .... various juveniles

> NOTE: **Juvenile geophilomorphs** may be identifiable through a combination of characters including the numbers of leg pairs (which remain the same throughout development), presence or absence of carpophagous pits, etc. however in some cases clear separation of species is difficult even to those with experience. Refer to the tabular key for assistance (p. 28).

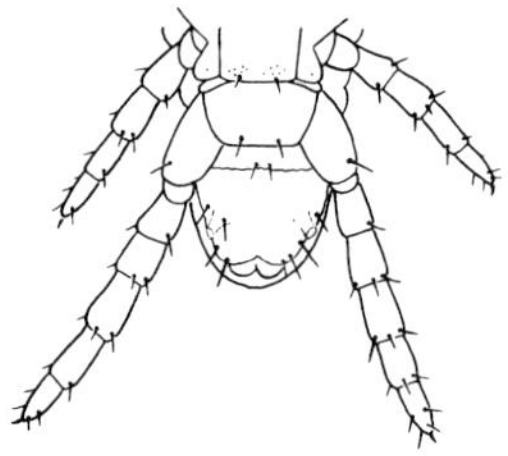

Fig. 37

-          Two or more pores on last legs 14

14 (13) Two obvious coxal pores on last legs (Fig. 38). Very rarely a minute additional one in centre of coxa 15

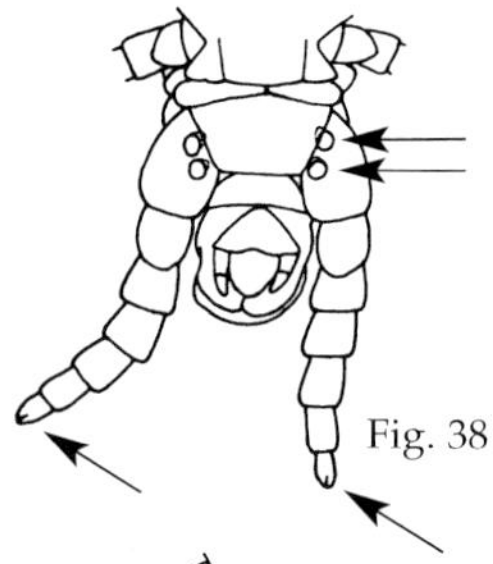

Fig. 38

-          More than two coxal pores on last legs (Fig. 39) 22

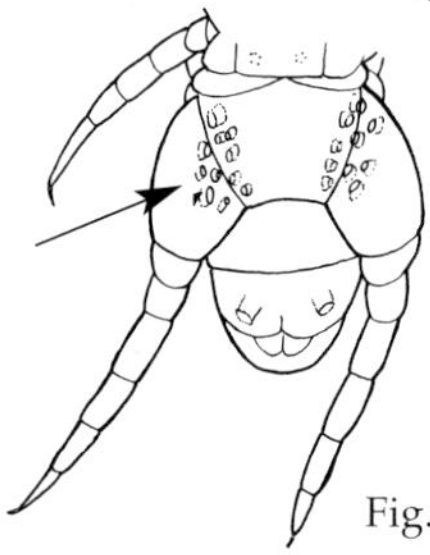

Fig. 39

15 (14) Terminal legs with distinct claws (Fig. 38) 16

-          Terminal legs without distinct claws or rudimentary only (Fig. 40) or with a transparent, spine-bearing tubercle (Fig. 41). No strongly marked sternal gutters 17

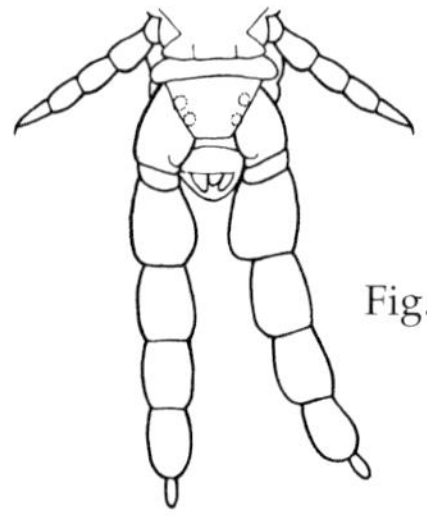

Fig. 40

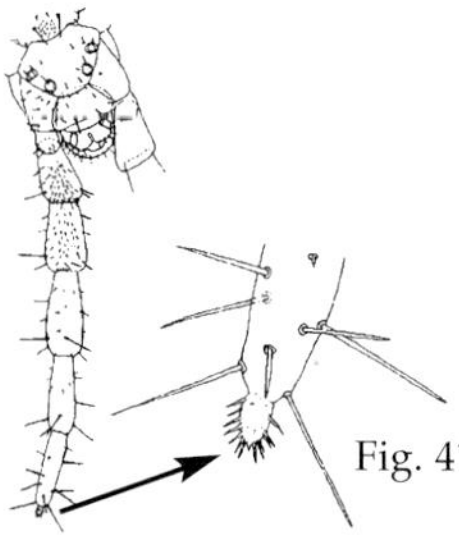

Fig. 41

16 (15) 37-41 pairs of legs. Anterior trunk sternites with three longitudinal gutters (grooves running the length of the sternite). Small, creamy white/yellowish species, may be quite brownish when alive .... *Geophilus truncorum* (p. 37)

NOTES:

The sternal gutters are probably best seen when the animal is fairly dry and light is at an angle. *Geophilus truncorum* is the only British centipede species with such a small number of leg pairs, two coxal pores and distinct claws on the last legs.

Common in woodland, under bark and in litter, heathland, etc.

\-   45 or more leg pairs, sternal gutters may be present .... juvenile geophilids

NOTE: **Juvenile geophilomorphs** may be identifiable through a combination of characters including the numbers of leg pairs (which remain the same throughout development), presence or absence of carpophagous pits, etc. however in some cases clear separation of species is difficult even to those with experience. Refer to the tabular key (p. 28) for assistance.

17 (15) Last article of last legs with a transparent tubercle (protrusion) bearing spines but no claws (Fig. 41). Up to 12 mm long with 45 leg pairs .... *Arenophilus peregrinus* (p. 30)

NOTE: Scilly, Cornwall. Refer to species notes.

\-   Last article of last legs not as above, 39-57 leg pairs 18

NOTE: Includes widespread species.

18 (17) Basal node (tooth) of poison claw absent or rudimentary (Fig. 42), reddish brown, 45-53 pairs of legs .... *Hydroschendyla submarina* (p. 38)

NOTE: Exclusively littoral species, rock-crevices, etc.

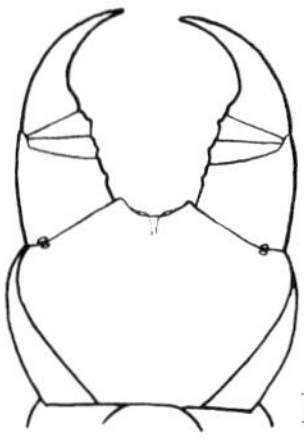

Fig. 42

\-   Basal node of poison claw present (as in Fig. 43), pale species 19

NOTE: Terrestrial or littoral.

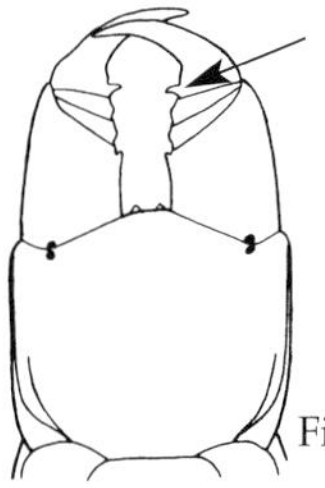

Fig. 43

19 (18) 51-57 pairs of legs, no pore groups on sternites ....
.... *Schendyla monoeci* (p. 41)

NOTES:

Unlikely to be seen. Single glasshouse record only, from Cornwall.

Sternal pores are not always easy to see and are best viewed when a preserved specimen has been allowed to dry somewhat.

-            39-49 pairs of legs, with or without sternal pore groups 20

20 (19) 39 pairs of legs, prominent tooth at base of poison claw,
another on the femoroid of the forcipule (Fig. 44). Poison
claw with smooth concavity. No sternal pore groups. Last
article of last legs very short (Fig. 45). Up to 12 mm ....
.... *Schendyla dentata* (p. 41)

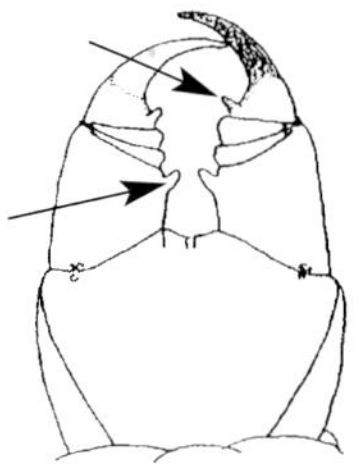

NOTES:

Recorded from a variety of mostly synanthropic sites in or on soil; widespread in Southern Britain and recorded as far north as Edinburgh but often overlooked because of its small size (12 mm).

Schendyla dentata has such distinctive forcipules and last legs that have a last article very short and less than one seventh of preceding that it is quite distinctively different from the other two *Schendyla* species even without seeing whether sternal pores are present.

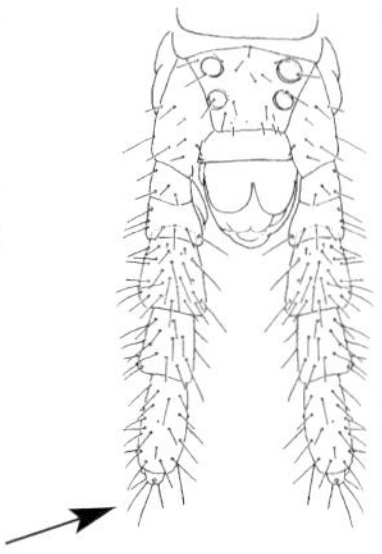

-            37-49 pairs of legs, lacks characteristic femoroid projection,
sternal pores present but may not be easily seen 21

21 (20) Poison claw with crenulate concavity (4-5 flattened teeth)
(Fig. 46). Last article of last legs (metatarsus) only one fifth
to one third length of preceding (tarsus). Telopodite (i.e. the
rest of the leg beyond the basal segment (coxa) less than 1.5
times as long as that of preceding leg (Fig. 47) ....
.... *Schendyla peyerimhoffi* (p. 42)

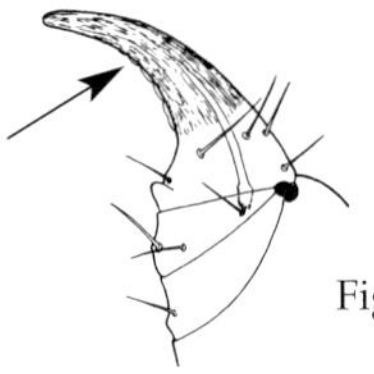

See NOTES opposite.

Fig. 44

Fig. 45

Fig. 46

telopodite

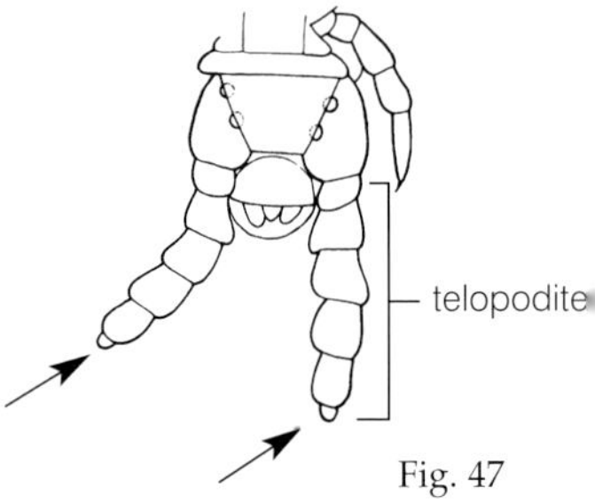

Fig. 47

- Poison claw with smooth concavity or with a few irregular incisures (Fig. 48). Last article of last legs about one third to one half length of the preceding. Telopodite more than 1.5 times as long as that of preceding leg. (Fig. 49) .... *Schendyla nemorensis* (p. 41)

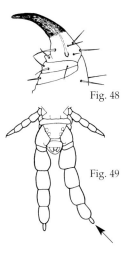

Fig. 48

Fig. 49

NOTES:

Usually the last legs of *S. peyerimhoffi* are markedly squatter and apparently fatter than *S. nemorensis*.

S. peyerimhoffi is known from littoral sites on the south and west coast from Sussex to Anglesey and has not been recorded inland in Britain whereas *S. nemorensis* is a widespread terrestrial species also sometimes found at the coast.

22 (14) Less than 41 leg pairs 23

- More than 41 leg pairs 24

23 (22) Without basal node (tooth) on poison claw (Fig. 50), 6-10 coxal pores on last legs adjacent to metasternite and a single isolated pore on the main part of the coxa (Fig. 51). Rather short and stout animals (20 mm x 1.6 mm) somewhat resembling 'one of the longer species cut in half' .... *Eurygeophilus pinguis* (p. 31)

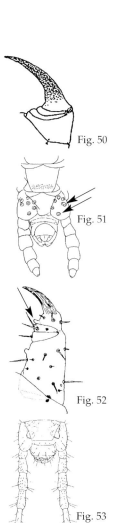

Fig. 50

Fig. 51

NOTES:

The poison claw has been described as 'flattened like the blade of a sabre'.

North Devon area where it is fairly widespread in a variety of sites.

Previously known as *Chalandea pinguis*.

- With clear basal node (tooth) on poison claw (Fig. 52), 3-5 coxal pores on last legs, no isolated pore (Fig. 53). Rather small species (13 mm) .... *Nothogeophilus turki* (p. 40)

NOTE: Rare, south and west coasts.

Fig. 52

Fig. 53

24 (22) 65-75 leg pairs. Coxal pores of last legs open both dorsally and ventrally (Fig. 54) .... *Geophilus electricus* (p. 33)

NOTE: Widespread, often in urban areas.

Fig. 54

- Less than 65 leg pairs. Coxal pores of last legs open ventrally only 25

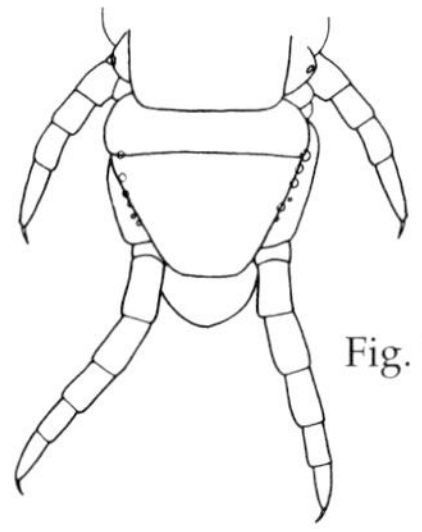

25 (24) Without a carpophagus structure although pegs (but not fossae) may be present (Fig. 55) 26

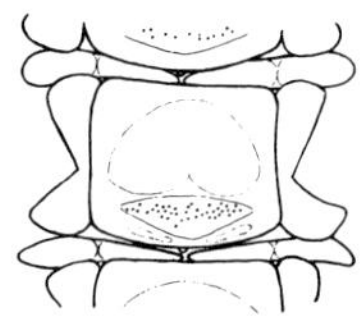

Fig. 55

- With carpophagus structure (pegs and fossae) present on anterior segments (Figs 56, 57) 27

NOTE: The 'carpophagus structure' comprises an arrangement on a series of the anterior mid trunk sternites where a 'peg' projecting backwards from one sternite is matched by a 'fossa' (pit) on the next. The width of this pit may be as little as under one half to as much as three-quarters of the width of the sternite. This structure may be very conspicuous as in *Geophilus carpophagus* and *Geophilus easoni* or less so as in some paler species.

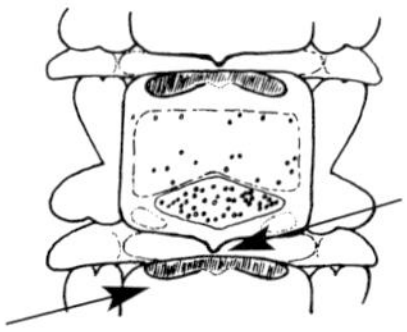

Fig. 56

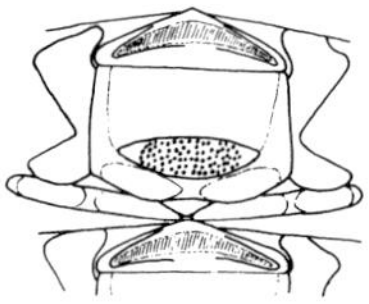

Fig. 57

26 (25) Poison claw with smooth concavity (Fig. 58). 3 coxal pores on last leg (Fig. 59). Small, pale species up to 13 mm long .... *Geophilus pusillifrater* (p. 36)

NOTE: All records so far are from coastal sites (Sussex, Cornwall, Isles of Scilly).

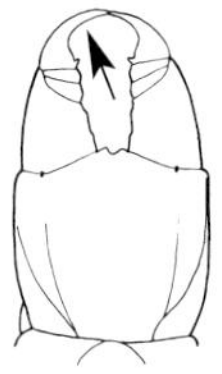

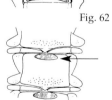

Fig. 58

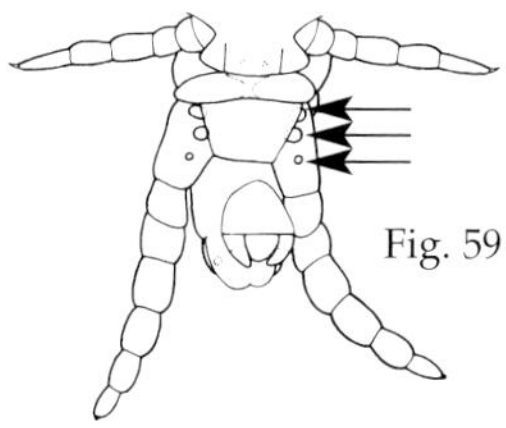

Fig. 59

\-   Poison claw with crenulate concavity (about 30-40 rounded scallops) (Fig. 60). 6-10 coxal pores on last leg (Fig. 61). Relatively robust, species up to 45 mm long .... *Geophilus flavus* (p. 33)

NOTES:

The relatively long antennae with their long segments is characteristic and is reflected in its former name of *Necrophloeophagus longicornis*. Other species of *Geophilus* in which the carpophagus structure is not seen clearly may be mistaken for this species.

Widespread and common in many parts of the British Isles.

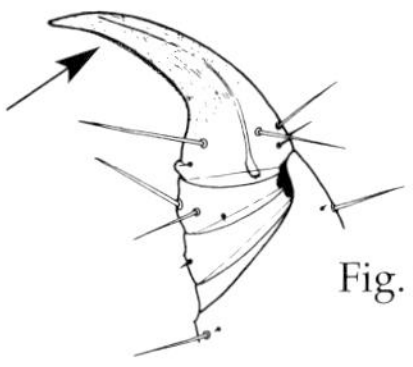

Fig. 60

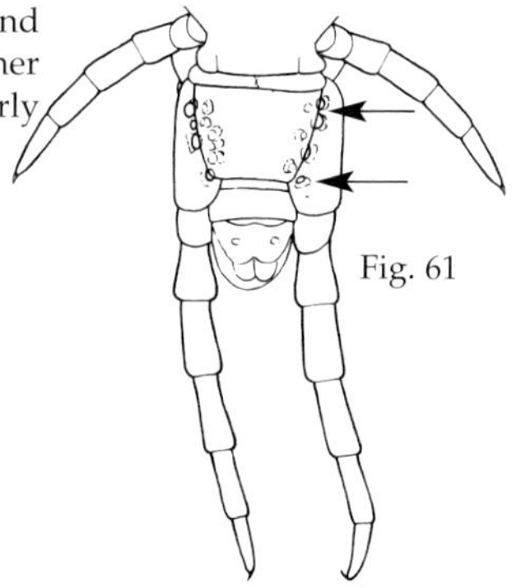

Fig. 61

27 (25) Carpophagus fossae (pits) occupying almost the whole breadth of the sternite (Fig. 62) 28

NOTE: Yellowish or whitish species.

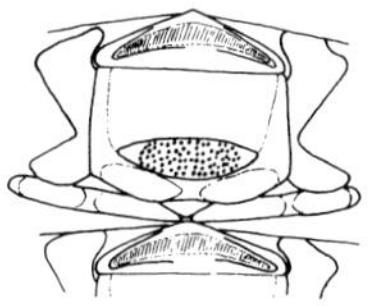

Fig. 62

\-   Carpophagus fossae occupying at most up to ¾ breadth of the sternite (Fig. 63) 29

NOTE: White, yellowish or red-brownish species.

Fig. 63

28 (27) Coxal pores of last legs along the edge of the metasternite, no isolated pore (Fig. 64). Second maxillae with a normal claw (Fig. 65) .... *Geophilus proximus* (p. 36)

NOTE: Shetlands, one record.

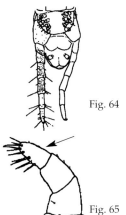

Fig. 64

Fig. 65

\-   Coxal pores of last legs along the edge of the metasternite plus an isolated single pore on the main body of the coxa (Fig. 66). Second maxillae with a small peg, not a claw (Fig. 67) .... *Geophilus insculptus* (p. 34)

NOTES:

The second maxillae may be seen by moving the poison claws out of the way when structures resembling those in Fig. 65 may be seen. Shining a bright light on or through a specimen mounted under a cover-slip on a microscope slide using a x40 or x100 magnification is often helpful.

Widespread species, often very common.

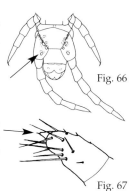

Fig. 66

Fig. 67

29 (27) Poison claw with a smooth concavity (Fig. 68). Carpophagus fossae conspicuous and nearly half the width of the sternite (Fig. 69). Relatively robust reddish brown or sometimes greyish/purplish animals 30

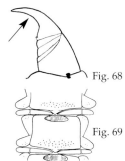

Fig. 68

Fig. 69

\-   Poison claw with a crenulate concavity (Fig. 70). Relatively slender whitish or yellowish species 31

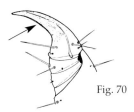

Fig. 70

30 (29) 47-49 leg pairs in males, 47-51 in females, coxal pores of last legs 6-12, 'tan' or chestnut colour throughout. Up to 40 mm .... *Geophilus easoni* (p. 32)

NOTE: Common on acid heathland; also found in grassland and woodland and in other generally 'rural' sites. (Also see NOTES below.)

- 51-55 leg pairs in males, 53-57 in females, coxal pores of last legs 4-8, anterior and posterior ends tan but trunk segments greeenish or brownish grey, sometimes with a hint of purple, up to 60 mm .... *Geophilus carpophagus* (in the strict sense) (p. 31)

NOTES:

Often coastal, arboreal or synanthropic.

A recently separated pair of species whose full ecology and distribution has not yet been worked out.

31 (29) Poison claw with about 14 crenulations (Fig. 71) .... *Geophilus gracilis* (p. 34)

NOTE: Estuarine and coastal species. (Also see NOTES below.)

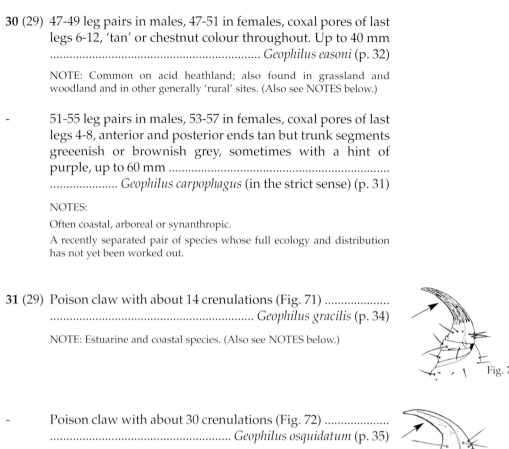

Fig. 71

- Poison claw with about 30 crenulations (Fig. 72) .... *Geophilus osquidatum* (p. 35)

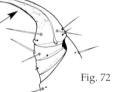

Fig. 72

NOTES:

Terrestrial but may be found coastally. Tendency to occur in SW regions of Britain.

These two species are not always easy to tell apart; refer to the species notes. *G. gracilis* seems to be exclusively littoral.

A relatively high magnification may be needed to see the crenulations clearly. Shining a bright light on or through a specimen mounted under a cover-slip on a microscope slide using a x40 or x100 magnification is often helpful.

A.D. BARBER

TABULAR KEY TO BRITISH GEOPHILOMORPHA

Species	Trunk segments	Coxal pores on last legs		Claw on last legs
		Number	**Position**	
Stigmatogaster souletina	93-101	∞	dorsal/ventral	
Stigmatogaster subterranea	77-83	∞	dorsal/ventral	
Geophilus electricus	65-73	10-18	dorsal/ventral	✔
Stenotaenia linearis	63-69	in pits	ventral	✔
Henia vesuviana	63-75	1 + pit	ventral	
Geophilus osquidatum	53-63	3-4	ventral	✔
Henia brevis	53-57	1 + pit	ventral	✔
Geophilus gracilis	51-57	4	ventral	✔
Geophilus carpophagus	51-57	4-8	ventral	✔
Schendyla monoeci	51-57	2	ventral	
Geophilus flavus	49-57	6-10	ventral	✔
Strigamia crassipes	49-53	15-30	ventral	✔
Strigamia maritima	47-51	10-15	ventral	✔
Geophilus easoni	47-51	6-12	ventral	✔
Mecistocephalus guildingii	49	∞	dorsal/ventral	
Geophilus proximus	45-55	8-10	ventral	✔
Geophilus insculptus	45-53	4-7 + 1	ventral	✔
Hydroschendyla submarina	45-53	2	ventral	
Tygarrup javanicus	45	c. 15	ventral/lateral	
Arenophilus peregrinus	45	2 (+1)	ventral	
Pachymerium ferrugineum	43-45	∞	dorsal/ventral	✔
Dicellophilus carniolensis	43	∞	dorsal/ventral	
Geophilus pusillifrater	41-43	1 + 2	ventral	✔
Schendyla peyerimhoffi	39-49	2	ventral	
Schendyla dentata	39	2	ventral	
Schendyla nemorensis	37-43	2	ventral	✔
Geophilus truncorum	37-41	2	ventral	✔
Strigamia acuminata	37-41	10-15	ventral	✔
Nothogeophilus turki	37-39	3-5	ventral	✔
Eurygeophilus pinguis	35-37	1 + 6-10	ventral	✔

Basal node on poison claw	Carpophagus structure	Sternal pore groups	Other notable features	Maximum length (mm)	Go to page
		✔	Sternal fossae	70	44
		✔	Virguliform fossae	70	44
✔	✔	✔	Dorsal coxal pores	40+	33
		✔	Usually synanthropic	55	43
		✔	Colour	50+	38
✔	✔	✔	Southern & western	30	35
		✔	Sternal pore areas	19	37
✔	✔	✔	Littoral	30	34
✔	✔	✔	Colour, size	60	31
			Greenhouse, once	22	41
✔		✔	Antennal articles	45	33
✔		✔	Colour, sternites	50	45
✔		✔	Colour, littoral	40	46
✔	✔	✔	Colour	40	32
			Hothouse	42	39
✔	✔	✔	Shetland, once	40	36
✔	✔	✔	Second maxillae	40	34
			Colour, littoral	40	38
			Hothouse	20	47
✔			Scillies, Cornwall	12	30
✔		✔	Coastal, rare	50	40
			Greenhouse, rare	60	30
✔		✔	SW coasts	13	36
		✔	Last legs, littoral	18	42
✔			Forcipules	12	41
	✔		Last legs	20	41
✔	✔		Last legs	20	37
✔		✔	Colour	30	45
✔		✔	South coasts, rare	13	40
	✔	✔	North Devon area	20	31

Species notes

Arenophilus peregrinus

Maximum length:	12 mm.
Trunk segments:	45.
Colour:	Yellowish white, head darker.
Head:	Longer than wide by a ratio of 8:7.
Antennae:	Twice as long as head capsule.
Forcipular tergite:	Barely trapeziform, weakly rounded borders.
Poison claw:	With basal tooth and crenulate concavity.
Trunk:	Sternites without fossae or similar structures, anterior pore fields oval or slightly reniform.
Last leg-bearing segment:	Two coxal pores opening beneath adjacent lateral edge of metasternite and one minute pore on ventral surface of each coxa. Legs weakly swollen, no claw but a hyaline swollen tubercle.
Diagnostic features:	Tubercle on last legs rather than claw.
Distribution:	Isles of Scilly, Cornwall.

Dicellophilus carniolensis

Maximum length:	60 mm.
Trunk segments:	43 (both sexes).
Colour:	Reddish-yellow, anterior end darker.
Shape:	Fairly stout, about 26 times as long as broad.
Head:	About 1.3 times as long as broad, broadest at front.
Antennae:	2.5 to 3 times breadth of head.
Forcipular segment:	Viewed from above the head can be seen to be markedly narrower than the width of the poison claws, this with the extreme narrowness of the trapezoidal tergite gives the whole anterior end a distinctive appearance. Femoroid, tibia and tarsus of poison claw each with a distal medial tooth.
Poison claw:	No basal node, concavity crenulate.
Trunk:	First pair of legs markedly smaller than others. No sternal pore groups.
Last leg-bearing segment:	One larger coxal pore in the middle of a mass of smaller ones. Dorsal as well as ventral pores.
Juveniles:	One large pore with 0-many small ones.

Diagnostic features:	Shape of anterior end, coxal pores. Compare with *Tygarrup*.
Distribution:	Old records from a garden in Lanarkshire and from greenhouses in Edinburgh and Northumberland.

Eurygeophilus pinguis (Plate 1, p. 93)

Maximum length:	20 mm.
Trunk segments:	35 (males), 37 (females).
Colour:	Pale yellowish brown.
Shape:	Very short in relation to breadth (1.6 mm).
Head:	Small in relation to body, slightly wider than long.
Antennae:	Relatively long, 3 to 4 times breadth of head.
Forcipular tergite:	Short, about 3 to 4 times as wide as long, sides curved, convergent posteriorly.
Poison claw:	Contracted towards base and without tooth.
Trunk:	Weak carpophagus structure present, pores on all segments except last.
Last leg-bearing segment:	6-10 coxal pores, mostly clearly visible, one pore more or less isolated distally. Legs of male rather swollen. Terminal claws well developed in females, seemingly less so in males because of the relatively swollen leg segments.
Juveniles:	Fewer coxal pores.
Diagnostic features:	Body shape ('like half a *Stigmatogaster*'), trunk segments, poison claw shape, coxae of last legs. Unlikely to be confused with any other of our species. Has a tendency to be often found curled up in a ball with its sternites pointing outwards rather in the way of *Henia vesuviana*.
Distribution:	Variety of sites, seemingly associated with deciduous trees. Widespread in North Devon.

Also known as *Chalandea pinguis*.

Geophilus carpophagus (sensu strictu) (Plate 2, p. 93)

Maximum length:	Up to 60 mm.
Trunk segments:	51-55 (males), 53-57 (females).
Colour:	Reddish brown head, forcipular segment and posterior end but trunk segments greenish-grey or brownish-grey, sometimes with a tinge of purple.
Shape:	Stouter and more attenuated anteriorly than other species of *Geophilus*, about 28-30 times longer than broad.
Head:	Barely longer than broad.

Antennae:	About 3.5 times as long as breadth of head and about one twelfth body length.
Forcipular tergite:	Sides slightly rounded, broader posteriorly than at front.
Poison claw:	Small tooth and smooth concavity.
Trunk:	Carpophagus pits conspicuous, nearly half width of sternite.
Last leg-bearing segment:	Coxae with 4-8 pores barely visible in live or uncleared specimens, normally covered by margin of sternal plate.
Diagnostic features:	Colour, appearance of the carpophagus fossae on trunk, coxae of last legs. Number of leg-pairs.
Distribution:	Coastal, arboreal and synanthropic.

Geophilus easoni

Maximum length:	40 mm.
Trunk segments:	47-49 (males), 49-51 (females).
Colour:	More or less uniform chestnut brown.
Shape:	Stouter and more attenuated anteriorly than many other species of *Geophilus*, about 28 to 30 times longer than broad.
Head:	Slightly longer than broad.
Antennae: body	About 3.4 times as long as breadth of head and about one twelfth length.
Forcipular tergite:	Sides slightly rounded, broader posteriorly than at front.
Poison claw:	Small tooth and smooth concavity.
Trunk:	Carpophagus pits conspicuous, nearly half width of sternite.
Last leg-bearing segment:	Coxae with 6-12 pores opening ventrally in two irregular rows parallel to edge of metasternite on each side and usually clearly visible. Legs of males much swollen.
Juveniles:	Youngest has no coxal pores at all then number increases with stages.
Diagnostic features:	Colour, appearance of the carpophagus fossae on trunk, coxae of last legs, leg numbers.
Distribution:	From the Scillies to Orkney. Ireland, Channel Islands. Common on acid heathland and elsewhere.

The two forms of *Geophilus carpophagus* are now regarded as separate species, *G. easoni* (the so-called 'short' form and the one described in Eason's 1964 *Centipedes of the British Isles*) and *Geophilus carpophagus* (the so-called 'long form').

Geophilus electricus (Plate 3, p. 93)

Maximum length:	40 mm or more.
Trunk segments:	65-69 (males), 67-73 (females).
Colour:	Pale yellow, anterior end a little darker.
Shape:	Rather slender, about 40 times longer than broad.
Head:	About 1.1 times as long as broad.
Antennae:	About three times breadth of head and one eighteenth body length.
Forcipular tergite:	Slightly curved edges, trapezoidal.
Poison claw:	Small basal tooth.
Trunk:	Carpophagus fossae occupy as much as three quarters the width of sternite. Pore areas diamond shaped.
Last leg-bearing segment:	4-6 pores opening dorsally, 6-12 ventrally with one isolated coxal pore.
Juveniles:	Single ventral coxal pore in youngest.
Diagnostic features:	Trunk segments, carpophagus fossa, dorsal coxal pores. Differs from *G. insculptus* in having more trunk segments, dorsal coxal pores and a normal tooth on the second maxillae.
Distribution:	Often in synanthropic sites. Not yet recorded from northern Scotland. Ireland.

Geophilus flavus

Maximum length:	45 mm.
Trunk segments:	49-55 (males), 51-57 (females).
Colour:	Bright yellow with anterior end distinctly darker.
Shape:	Usually rather more than 30 times as long as broad.
Head:	About 1.2 times as long as broad.
Antennae:	About 5 times breadth of head and one tenth body length. Articles very elongate.
Forcipular tergite:	Lateral borders slightly curved, trapezoidal.
Poison claw:	Small basal node and about 30-40 rounded scallops internally.
Trunk:	Pegs, resembling those of many other species of *Geophilus* are present but no corresponding carpophagus fossae.
Last leg-bearing segment:	6-10 pores opening along edge of metasternite. Legs of male slightly swollen. Apical claws distinct.
Juveniles:	One or more coxal pores.

| Diagnostic features: | The long antennae, darker front end and rather elongate antennal articles distinguish it but it resembles the generally less common *Geophilus osquidatum* and *Geophilus gracilis*. The latter have carpophagus fossae. |
| Distribution: | Urban and rural sites of a wide variety of types including sea shore. Widespread and often very common up to Scotland except the far north and with an apparent eastern tendency. Ireland. |

Also known as *Necrophloeophagus longicornis*.

Geophilus gracilis (Plate 4, p. 93)

Maximum length:	30 mm.
Trunk segments:	51-53 (males), 51-57 (females).
Colour:	Yellowish with anterior end darker.
Shape:	35-40 times longer than broad.
Head:	About 1.1 times as long as broad.
Antennae:	5 or 6 times breadth of head, articles very elongate.
Forcipular tergite:	Trapezoidal.
Poison claw:	Small basal node, about 14 rather flattened scallops on inner edge.
Trunk:	Carpophagus fossae occupy up to three quarters the breadth of sternite.
Last leg-bearing segment:	4 coxal pores opening ventrally along edge of metasternite, sometimes a 5th. Legs may have a minute tubercle rather than a claw. Legs of males slightly swollen.
Diagnostic features:	Resembles *G. osquidatum* but differs in only 14 scallops in poison claw and tends to have slightly more coxal pores. Carpophagus fosssae, forcipules, last segment, habitat.
Distribution:	A seashore species found under stones on mud and in other microhabitats. Probably quite widespread. Kent to Cornwall, Wales, W. Scotland, Isle of Man, Ireland.

Eason (1964) described this as *Geophilus fucorum seurati*, a name given to a form from the Algerian coast. Our species could be synonymous with *Geophilus algarum* Brolemann which occurs on the French coast.

Geophilus insculptus

Maximum length:	30 mm (but may be up to 40 mm).
Trunk segments:	45-49 (males), 49-53 (females).
Colour:	Pale yellow, anterior end darker.
Shape:	About 35 times longer than broad.

Head:	Barely longer than broad.
Antennae:	About 3.5 times breadth of head, one thirteenth body length. Articles somewhat elongate.
Forcipular tergite:	Barely trapeziform, lateral borders strongly rounded but much broader posteriorly.
Poison claw:	Small basal tooth, concavity smooth.
Trunk:	Carpophagus fossae up to nine tenths of breadth of sternite, more or less sickle shaped or triangular.
Last leg-bearing segment:	4-7 ventral coxal pores along edge of metasternite with one isolated pore. Legs of male somewhat swollen. Claws distinct.
Juveniles:	Single or two coxal pores.
Diagnostic features:	Shape of carpophagus fossae, last leg-bearing segment (*G. electricus* has dorsal as well as ventral pores), second maxillae have a peg and not a claw.
Distribution:	Widespread in a variety of urban and rural habitats. Across most of Britain but seems to have a northerly and easterly tendency in England.

Geophilus alpinus Meinert has been shown to be the earlier and therefore, possibly, the more correct name of this species. The name *Geophilus oligopus* has also, incorrectly, been used for this species.

Geophilus osquidatum

Maximum length:	30 mm.
Trunk segments:	53-55 (males), 55-63 (females).
Colour:	Yellow with anterior region darker.
Shape:	About 40 times longer than broad.
Head:	About 1.1 times as long as broad.
Antennae:	About 5 or 6 times breadth of head and one ninth body length. Articles very elongate.
Forcipular tergite:	Trapezoidal with slightly curved or straight lateral edges.
Poison claw:	With basal node and about 30 rounded scallops.
Trunk:	Carpophagus fossae up to two thirds breadth of sternite. Pore areas transversely triangular.
Last leg-bearing segment:	3-4 pores on each coxa adjacent to edge of metasternite. Legs of male slightly swollen, claws of legs distinct.
Diagnostic features:	Needs to be distinguished from *G. gracilis* and *Geophilus flavus*, both of which have similar antennae. Carpophagus fossae, concavity of poison claw, last trunk segment. *G. gracilis* is exclusively maritime.
Distribution:	A variety of sites, including gardens, from the South-West and adjacent areas as far east as Kent. Ireland.

Geophilus proximus

Maximum length:	40 mm.
Trunk segments:	45-51 (males), 45-55 (females).
Colour:	Pale yellowish, anterior end darker.
Head:	Somewhat longer than broad.
Antennae:	2.5 times length of head.
Forcipular tergite:	Sides curved.
Poison claw:	Clear basal tooth.
Trunk:	Pore areas diamond shaped (in *G. insculptus* they are spindle shaped). Carpophagus structure present.
Last leg-bearing segment:	Coxal pores 8-10 along edge of metasternite. No isolated pore.
Diagnostic features:	Distinguished from *G. insculptus* by arrangement of coxal pores and by the second maxillae having a distinct claw.
Distribution:	A single specimen has been collected from Unst, Shetlands.

Older references to *G. proximus* in Britain undoubtedly refer to *Geophilus insculptus*.

Geophilus pusillifrater

Maximum length:	13 mm.
Trunk segments:	41 (males), 43 (females).
Colour:	Pale, with head a little darker.
Shape:	30 to 35 times as long as broad.
Head:	About 1.3 times as long as broad, almost rectangular.
Antennae:	About five times as long as breadth of head, one eighth length of body.
Forcipular tergite:	Slightly rounded sides, trapezoidal.
Poison claw:	Fairly prominent basal node, concavity smooth.
Trunk:	No carpophagus structure, pore groups diffuse.
Last leg-bearing segment:	Two coxal pores and one smaller one further back towards the apex of the coxa. Apical claws distinct in female, reduced to tubercle in male.
Diagnostic features:	Trunk segments, lack of carpophagus structure, pores of last coxae.
Distribution:	Shingle and rock crevices, Sussex, Cornwall, Scillies.

It is suspected that this name, given to a poorly described single specimen from Bosnia-Herzegovina, is not the correct name for this species (*L. Bonato*, pers. comm.)

Geophilus truncorum

Maximum length:	20 mm (but usually 12-14 mm).
Trunk segments:	37-39 (males), 39-41 (females).
Colour:	Pale yellow to pale brown, head a little darker.
Shape:	20 to 25 times as long as broad.
Head:	About as long as broad.
Antennae:	About 2.5 to 3 times breadth of head capsule, one twelfth body length.
Forcipular tergite:	Borders slightly rounded or more or less straight, trapezoidal.
Poison claw:	Small tooth at base of claw, concavity smooth.
Trunk:	Three longitudinal depressions (gutters) on anterior sternites. Carpophagus pits occupy just over half width. No sternal pore groups.
Last leg-bearing segment:	Coxae each with two pores. Legs of male moderately swollen. Apical claws distinct.
Juveniles:	One or two coxal pores on each side.
Diagnostic features:	Size, segment number, last legs with two coxal pores and distinct claws. *Schendyla nemorensis* is similar but lacks carpophagus structure and last legs have no claws.
Distribution:	Common in woodland in litter and under bark, grassland, moorland. Favours rural sites generally. Widespread from Scillies to Shetlands. Ireland.

Henia brevis

Maximum length:	19 mm.
Trunk segments:	53-57.
Colour:	Whitish-yellow.
Shape:	About 25 times longer than broad – notably elongate compared with other small pale geophilomorphs.
Head:	About 0.9 times as long as broad.
Antennae:	About 3.5 times breadth of head, articles rather broader than long.
Forcipular tergite:	Markedly curved sides, about as wide at the front as posteriorly.
Poison claw:	Relatively slender and without clear basal node.
Trunk:	No carpophagus structure. The pore group is quite distinct, narrow and oblong with the longitudinal axis parallel to the sides of the sternite.
Last leg-bearing segment:	A single large pore adjacent to the metasternite and several smaller pores opening into a pit at the base of the coxa. Legs of male very swollen.

Diagnostic features:	Trunk segments, shape of head and forcipular tergite, sternal pore groups, last segments. A much smaller and paler animal than *H. vesuviana*.
Distribution:	Mostly from synanthropic sites, southern England.

Formerly known as *Chaetechelyne montana oblogocribellata*. British animals have 53-57 pairs of legs whereas the figures given for Italian and French specimens in the literature are 45-47. However it does seem to be similar in other respects to Verhoeff's type.

Henia vesuviana (Plate 5, p. 94)

Maximum length:	50 mm (foreign specimens have been recorded up to 95 mm).
Trunk segments:	63-67 (males), 69-75 (females) (57-75, 59-87 in foreign specimens).
Colour:	Anterior and posterior ends light reddish brown. Within the trunk region may be seen the body contents which are greenish grey with a distinct white line down the centre. This latter is the dorsal blood vessel which, in a live animal, may be seen contracting and relaxing.
Shape:	Stout, especially females. 18 to 23 times as long as broad.
Head:	About 0.85 times as long as broad.
Antennae:	About 3.5 times breadth of head and one-seventeenth body length. Articles about as long as broad.
Forcipular tergite:	Strongly curved sides, front about as wide as posterior.
Poison claw:	No distinct basal node.
Trunk:	Pore groups clearly seen, circular or slightly oval.
Last leg-bearing segment:	Coxae swollen. One large pore adjacent to metasternite and a group of small pores opening into a pit at the base of the coxa. Legs of male much swollen and usually without claws.
Diagnostic features:	Colour, shape, shape of head and forcipular tergite, sternites, last segment. A very distinctive animal. It may sometimes be found in soil curled up into a tight ball with the sternites facing outwards.
Distribution:	A variety of sites including upper shore above tide line. Southern England especially along the coast, London area, Bristol.

A characteristic habit is to be found curled up into a ball in soil with the sternites and their glands to the outside, presumably as a defensive posture as these glands produce a sticky secretion.

Formerly known as *Chaetechelyne vesuviana*.

Hydroschendyla submarina

Maximum length:	40 mm.
Trunk segments:	45-51 (males), 47-53 (females).
Colour:	Reddish brown.
Shape:	About 25 times as long as broad, fairly stout.

Head:	About 1.25 times as long as broad.
Antennae:	About 4 times breadth of head, one tenth body length.
Forcipular tergite:	Trapezoidal.
Poison claw:	Basal node absent or inconspicuous, concavity with about 5 well spaced incisures which may give it a crenulate appearance.
Trunk:	No sternal pore groups.
Last leg-bearing segment:	Two coxal pores, legs of both sexes rather swollen. There may be a tubercle (not a claw) at the end.
Diagnostic features:	Differs from our other schendylids in size, colour, trunk segments, etc. Superficially somewhat like *Strigamia maritima* from similar habitats but the two coxal pores and lack of a strong projection at the base of the poison claw distinguish easily.
Distribution:	A maritime species from sea shores, rock crevices, etc. at or below high water mark. Probably under-recorded. South-West England, South Wales, possibly Yorkshire. Ireland, Channel Islands.

Mecistocephalus guildingii

Maximum length:	42 mm.
Trunk segments:	49.
Colour:	Bright yellow, anterior end red-brown.
Shape:	Fairly stout, about 26 times as long as broad.
Antennae:	About twice as long as head.
Head:	Very elongate, about twice as long as wide.
Forcipular segment:	Viewed from above the head can be seen to be markedly narrower than the width of the poison claws (about 1:1.6), this with the extreme narrowness of the tergite (about two thirds that of the width of the head) gives the whole anterior end a very distinctive appearance. Femoroid with two medial teeth, tibia and tarsus of poison claw each with a medial tooth.
Poison claw:	Very small basal node, concavity smooth.
Trunk:	First pair of legs markedly smaller than others. No sternal pore groups.
Last leg-bearing segment:	Numerous small pores, dorsally and ventrally.
Diagnostic features:	Shape of anterior end, segment number. Compare with *Tygarrup*.
Distribution:	Recorded only from the Moist Tropical Biome at the Eden Project, Cornwall.

L. Bonato has identified this as likely to be *L. guildingii* from the Atlantic coasts of tropical Americas and probably identical to a species from West Africa. It is described in detail (incorrectly named as *M. maxillaris*) by Brölemann (1930).

Nothogeophilus turki

Maximum length:	13 mm.
Trunk segments:	37-39.
Colour:	Yellowish white, head and poison claws darker.
Shape:	Anterior end slender, posterior fatter.
Head:	Longer than wide in ratio about 1.2 times as long as broad.
Antennae:	Long, filiform, about 3.5 times as long as head capsule.
Forcipular tergite:	Trapezoidal.
Poison claw:	Strong basal tooth and smooth concavity. Femoroid has a marked distal tooth internally.
Trunk:	No fossae or similar structures, pore areas more or less reniform.
Last leg-bearing segment:	3-5 coxal glands opening beneath lateral edge of sternite. Slightly swollen in males. Apical claws present.
Diagnostic features:	Size, trunk segments, forcipules, last segment.
Distribution:	Scilly Isles, Isle of Wight.

Pachymerium ferrugineum

Maximum length:	50 mm.
Trunk segments:	43 (males), 43-45 (females).
Colour:	Reddish yellow with anterior region darker.
Shape:	About 30 to 35 times longer than broad, barely attenuated anteriorly.
Head:	About 1.3 to 1.4 times as long as broad, almost rectangular in shape.
Antennae:	About four times as long as breadth of head and one tenth body length.
Forcipular tergite:	At its broadest, barely broader than head, about three quarters that of T1. Sides straight and strongly convergent anteriorly.
Poison claw:	With prominent, slightly hooked basal node.
Trunk:	Sternal pore groups do not lie in depressed or delineated areas, difficult to see.
Last leg-bearing segment:	Coxae long and narrow with numerous small pores both dorsally and ventrally.
Juveniles:	With reduced numbers of coxal pores.
Diagnostic features:	Colour, distinct appearance of head and forcipular tergite, numerous small coxal pores both dorsally and ventrally on last legs.
Distribution:	The few British records of this conspicuous species are from coastal sites, in shingle.

Schendyla dentata

Maximum length:	12 mm.
Trunk segments:	39 (only females known).
Colour:	Colourless, somewhat translucent.
Head:	About as long as broad.
Antennae:	3 to 4 times as long as breadth of head capsule, about one twelfth body length.
Forcipular tergite:	Trapezoidal.
Poison claw:	With prominent tooth at base and smooth concavity, also a prominent tooth on the femoroid.
Trunk:	Without fossae or pore areas.
Last leg-bearing segment:	Two coxal pores on each side, metatarsus (last segment) of leg about one seventh length of tarsus, truncated.
Juveniles:	1 + 1 coxal pores, antennae relatively short and stout.
Diagnostic features:	Appearance of forcipules with teeth on femoroid and appearance of last legs.
Distribution:	Under stones, in soil, etc. in a variety of urban and semi-urban sites across southern England from Devon to Norfolk. Inconspicuous and almost certainly under-recorded.

Also known as *Brachyschendyla dentata*.

Schendyla monoeci

Maximum length:	22 mm.
Trunk segments:	51-57 (only females known).
Colour:	Pale.
Head:	Longer than wide in ratio 8:7.
Antennae:	About three times longer than width of head capsule.
Poison claw:	Small basal node, concavity smooth or crenulate.
Trunk:	No sternal pore groups.
Last leg-bearing segment:	Two coxal pores, legs slender, last article longer than preceding, no claw.
Diagnostic features:	Appearance of last legs, no sternal pore groups, second maxillae claw with 1 or 2 spines.
Distribution:	Recorded once from a greenhouse in Cornwall.

Also known as *Brachyschendyla monoeci*.

Schendyla nemorensis

Maximum length:	20 mm.
Trunk segments:	37-41 (males), 39-43 (females).

Colour:	Colourless to pale yellow, anterior end a little darker.
Shape:	About 30 times longer than broad.
Head:	About 1.1 times as long as broad.
Antennae:	About 3 to 4 times breadth of head and one-fourteenth body length.
Forcipular tergite:	Trapezoidal.
Poison claw:	Small but distinct basal node, concavity usually smooth but sometimes with a few well spaced incisures.
Trunk:	No carpophagus fossae. Pore groups an irregular cluster.
Last leg-bearing segment:	Two coxal pores on each side, legs somewhat swollen in both sexes, last article being one third to one half length of preceding. No claw but there may be a minute spine.
Juveniles:	With one or two coxal pores.
Diagnostic features:	Number of trunk segments, appearance of last legs. Shape of last legs and absence of claw separates from *Geophilus truncorum* of similar size.
Distribution:	A variety of habitats including gardens and maritime sites. From the Scillies to Shetland but seemingly commoner in the South. Ireland, Channel Islands.

Schendyla peyerimhoffi

Maximum length:	18 mm.
Trunk segments:	39-45 (males), 41-49 (females).
Colour:	Colourless to pale yellow, anterior end a little darker.
Shape:	About 30 times longer than broad.
Head:	About 1.1 times as long as broad.
Antennae:	About 3 to 4 times breadth of head and one-fourteenth body length.
Forcipular tergite:	Trapezoidal.
Poison claw:	Small but distinct basal node, concavity with four or five well spaced incisures. In some individuals these are indistinct but the concavity is then irregular not smooth.
Trunk:	No carpophagus fossae. Pore groups narrower, more elongate and further forward than *S. nemorensis*.
Last leg-bearing segment:	Two coxal pores on each side, legs somewhat swollen in both sexes, last article being one fifth to one third length of preceding. The articles are relatively more squat than in *S. nemorensis* and so have the appearance of being more swollen. The inner margin of the prefemur tends to be more protuberant than in that species.

Diagnostic features:	Concavity of poison claw, appearance of last legs, habitat. Not always easy to separate from *S. nemorensis* which also can occur on the shore but the last legs are often rather distinctive.
Distribution:	A seashore species from under stones on muddy shores, rock crevices, etc. south and west coasts from Sussex to Anglesey, probably rather under-recorded.

Stenotaenia linearis

Maximum length:	55 mm.
Trunk segments:	Males 63-79, females 67-79.
Colour:	Yellow with anterior end darker.
Shape:	Only slightly attenuated.
Head:	About as long as broad.
Antennae:	2 to 2.5 times breadth of head, articles rather broader than long.
Forcipular tergite:	Short with sides slightly rounded, anterior end narrower than posterior.
Poison claw:	No basal node, concavity smooth.
Trunk:	No carpophagus structure. The anterior segments bear a very distinct round sternal pore area with a rim making them very easily seen compared with other species.
Last leg-bearing segment:	The coxal glands open into pits making them difficult to see in preserved animals unless they are cleared. In a living animal held in a transparent envelope it may be possible to see these quite clearly by holding it up to the light. Legs of similar degree of swelling in both sexes.
Juveniles:	In a 10mm juvenile it was possible to see distinct pore areas of a few pores and 2 pores on each terminal coxa corresponding to the pits of adults.
Diagnostic features:	Number of segments, shape of poison claws, pore areas on sternites, coxal pores opening into pits.
Distribution:	Synanthropic sites from Cornwall to Northumberland. Probably widespread in the London area. Often abundant where it occurs.

Formerly known as *Clinopodes linearis* or *Geophilus linearis*.

Stigmatogaster souletina

Maximum length:	70 mm.
Trunk segments:	93-95 (males), 97-101 (females).
Colour:	Pale yellow with anterior end a little darker.
Shape:	Resembles *Stigmatogaster subterranea* but more slender, body 40 times longer than wide.
Head:	About 0.9 times as long as broad.
Antennae:	About 3 times breadth of head, one twentieth body length.
Forcipular tergite:	Rounded sides, about the same width at the front as posteriorly.
Poison claw:	As *S. subterranea*.
Trunk:	Sternal pore groups as in *S. subterranea* . About five or six sternites from about S42 to S47 have a large transverse oval fossa posteriorly. Last leg-bearing segment: coxal pores small and numerous. Legs little swollen.
Juveniles:	Possibly the fossae are absent in the earliest juveniles.
Diagnostic features:	Trunk segment number, sternal fossae, coxae of last legs.
Distribution:	Recorded from two nearby sites in Cornwall.

Stigmatogaster subterranea (Plate 6, p. 94)

Maximum length:	60 mm (sometimes up to 70 mm).
Trunk segments:	77-81 (males), 79-83 (females).
Colour:	Yellow to pale brown, anterior end darker.
Shape:	Slender, about 40 times longer than broad.
Head:	About 0.8 times as long as broad.
Antennae:	Short and stout with short articles. About twice as long as breadth of head or slightly longer, and one twenty-fourth body length.
Forcipular tergite:	Sides strongly curved, nearly as wide at front as posteriorly.
Poison claw:	Blunt and inconspicuous basal node, smooth concavity.
Trunk:	Sternal pore groups fairly clear, circular, oval, reniform. About a dozen sternites in the mid region (roughly S26-S40) show small, comma-shaped fossae with thickened margins at the anterior sternal angle (virguliform fossae).
Last leg-bearing segment:	Numerous small coxal pores both dorsally and ventrally. Legs of males slightly swollen. No claws in either sex.
Juveniles:	With smaller numbers of coxal pores and virguliform fossae barely visible.

Diagnostic features:	Trunk segment number, coxal pores, sternites, antennae.
Distribution:	Often in synanthropic habitats over much of its range which extends to southern Scotland. A marked southern and western tendency; a common woodland animal in the South-West. Ireland, Channel Islands.

Strigamia acuminata (Plate 7, p. 94)

Maximum length:	30 mm.
Trunk segments:	37-39 (males), 41 (females).
Colour:	Red.
Shape:	About 20 times longer than broad.
Head:	About 0.85 to 0.95 times as long as broad, rounded shoulders.
Antennae:	About 3.5 to 4 times breadth of head and one ninth length of body.
Forcipular tergite:	About as broad as head, about the same or slightly broader than T1, sides convex.
Poison claw:	With prominent basal tooth (less prominent than *S. crassipes*).
Trunk:	Sternites with a transverse ridge less prominent than *S. crassipes*. No deep longitudinal median cleft but a shallow gutter.
Last leg-bearing segment:	Pleurites fused with adjacent pretergite. Coxae with 10-15 ventral pores. Legs of female slender, of male rather swollen.
Juveniles:	Similar to *S. crassipes* but with fewer trunk segments and coxal pores.
Diagnostic features:	Colour, large tooth at base of poison claw, numerous coxal pores on last legs, number of trunk segments (distinguish from *S. crassipes*). Note immature *S. crassipes* will have a reduced number of coxal pores so that other characters will need checking.
Distribution:	Often a woodland species. A distinctly southern species with no records from Scotland or Ireland.

Strigamia crassipes

Maximum length:	50 mm.
Trunk segments:	49-51 (males), 51-53 (females).
Colour:	Red.
Shape:	Fairly stout, about 25 times longer than broad.
Head:	About 0.85 to 0.90 times as long as broad, rounded shoulders.
Antennae:	About 2.5 to 3 times breadth of head and one eighteenth length of body.
Forcipular tergite:	Much broader than head, about the same as T1, sides convex.

Poison claw:	With very prominent basal tooth.
Trunk:	Sternites with a well marked transverse ridge. In front of this a deep longitudinal median cleft.
Last leg-bearing segment:	Pleurites fused with adjacent pretergite. Coxae with 15-30 pores ventrally. Legs of female slender, of male much swollen.
Juveniles:	One or more coxal pores visible on each side.
Diagnostic features:	Colour, very large tooth at base of poison claw, numerous coxal pores on last legs, number of trunk segments (distinguish from *S. accuminata*).
Distribution:	Often a woodland species. A distinctly southern species with relatively few records north of Mersey-Humber. Has been found in southern Scotland. Ireland.

Strigamia maritima (Plate 8, p. 94)

Maximum length:	40 mm.
Trunk segments:	47-49 (males), 49-51 (females).
Colour:	Red.
Shape:	About 27 times longer than broad, more slender than the other British *Strigamia* species.
Head:	About as long as broad, rounded shoulders.
Antennae:	About 3 times breadth of head and one twelfth length of body.
Forcipular tergite:	Barely broader than head, about the same as T1, sides convex.
Poison claw:	With prominent basal tooth.
Trunk:	No distinct transverse ridge on sternites. Centre of each sternite occupied by a shallow roughly circular depression.
Last leg-bearing segment:	Pleurites not fused with adjacent pretergites. Coxae with 10-15 ventral pores. Legs of female slender, of male rather swollen.
Juveniles:	With one or more coxal pores on each side.
Diagnostic features:	Colour, large tooth at base of poison claw, numerous coxal pores on last legs, number of trunk segments, appearance of last trunk segment, habitat. *Hydroschendyla submarina* has only two coxal pores on each side.
Distribution:	A seashore species found in shingle, rock crevices and under stones often in very large numbers. May occur some distance upstream in estuaries. Seashores from Cornwall to the Shetlands. Ireland. Channel Islands.

Tygarrup javanicus

Maximum length:	Up to 20 mm in 'wild' specimens.
Trunk segments:	45.
Colour:	Pale yellow, anterior end brownish-orange.
Head:	Longer than wide (ratio 1 to 0.8).
Forcipular tergite:	See description under *Dicellophillus carniolensis* for the characteristic appearance of members of the family (Mecistocephalidae). Basal segment and tibioid (but not femoroid) of poison claw with small teeth.
Poison claw:	Without basal node.
Last leg-bearing segment:	Coxae with about 15 pores opening on lateral and ventral surfaces. Without the single large median pore of *Dicellophilus*. In some specimens, especially some juveniles, the two innermost pores are markedly larger and at first glance the animal might be mistaken for a *Schendyla*.
Juveniles:	No pores on the coxae of a 7 mm specimen.
Diagnostic features:	Appearance of anterior end, trunk segments, coxal pores.
Distribution:	Specimens collected from a palm house at Kew, from a tropical greenhouse in Cornwall (where it was abundant) and an indoor 'tropical' location in Somerset.

All the Cornish specimens collected appeared to be females or immature.

The taxonomy of the group of species to which this animal belongs is confused so that this name is questionable (*L. Bonato*, pers.comm).

SPECIES OF DOUBTFUL STATUS IN THE BRITISH ISLES

Schendyla carniolensis

Maximum length:	27 mm.
Trunk segments:	37-47 (males), 41-49 (females).
Antennae:	2 .5 to 3 times longer than head.
Poison claw:	Prominent basal node, concavity smooth.
Last leg-bearing segment:	Two coxal pores beneath coxosternite. Last article of leg usually more than half length of preceding and surmounted by a small tubercle with or without a spine.
Diagnostic features:	Resembles *S. nemorensis* but the second maxillae have 1-3 spines on the internal edges of their claws and other detailed features.
Distribution:	Reported as occurring on the coasts of Devon and Dorset. No specimens have been found in recent years so possibly recorded in error or overlooked.

SCOLOPENDROMORPHA

All British Scolopendromorpha belong to the genus *Cryptops* and are brownish or light reddish brown in colour, up to 35 mm or more long and without ocelli. The forcipular coxosternite lacks teeth but instead bears several setae.

The head of *Cryptops* is circular to oval with at least a trace of a pair of dorsal paramedian sutures (grooves) running from the bases of the antennae (near the outer edge) to the central part of the posterior margin (Figs 73, 74). The antennae are composed of about 17 articles, sometimes less. The labrum is a well defined structure with large, well defined side-pieces and a narrow mid-piece (Fig. 75). In *C. parisi* the side-pieces are notched so that there appears to be five teeth in the centre of the labrum including the mid-piece (Fig. 76).

There is no separate forcipular tergite, that being fused with the first trunk tergite and referred to here as T1. This tergite has a conspicuous series of sutures on it in *C. anomalans*, forming a diagonal cross shape (cruciform suture) and is best seen on a dry specimen with the light at an angle (Fig. 74).

The forcipular coxosternite is about twice as broad as long, narrowed posteriorly and with more or less protuberant anterior borders between the poison claws with several stout setae (Fig. 77). The poison claw has a smooth concavity and an inconspicuous basal node.

Fig. 73. Dorsal paramedian sutures on head of *Cryptops hortensis*.

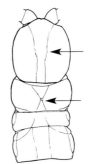

Fig. 74. Dorsal paramedian sutures on head and cruciform suture on T1 for *Cryptops anomalans*.

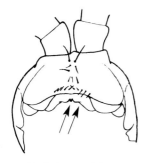

Fig. 75. Labrum with narrow mid-piece and well defined side-pieces of *Cryptops hortensis*.

Fig. 76. Labrum with notched side-pieces of *Cryptops parisi*.

Fig. 77. Forcipular coxosternite of *Cryptops hortensis*.

There are 21 trunk segments, each bearing a pair of legs gradually increasing in size to the 20th. The tergites show an alternation of small and large in the anterior region but this is far less marked than in *Lithobius*. The last trunk segments bear legs markedly larger than the others (Fig. 78) and there is a tendency for these to be shed. Since these legs are very valuable in diagnosis of species they should be kept with the specimen if at all possible; they are one of the most reliable ways of separating our species.

On the last pair of legs the coxal pores are small and very numerous and confined to a well defined ventral area, the cribriform area (Figs 79, 80). The distribution of spines and setae in relation to this may be important (Fig. 80). The remainder of the leg comprises five articles (there is no trochanter). The ventral margins of the tibia and tarsus bear serrate combs (Fig. 81) which, when the leg is flexed, are opposed to one another. The characteristics of these combs are valuable in separating our species. Unfortunately the legs have a tendency to flex up when animals are preserved; it may be helpful to straighten these out once the animals are killed before they become fixed in position to make future examination easier.

The terminal segments are poorly chitinised and the sexual structures are of no value in distinguishing the species.

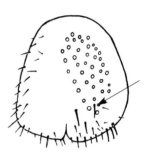

Fig. 80. Right last coxa of *Cryptops hortensis*, showing single seta amongst pores.

Fig. 78. *Cryptops hortensis* ♀.

Fig. 79. Right last leg of *Cryptops hortensis* ♀ showing ventral groove on prefemur. The leg has been rotated to show much of its lateral aspect.

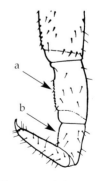

Fig. 81. Right last leg of *Cryptops parisi* showing serrate combs

KEY TO BRITISH SCOLOPENDROMORPHA

1. T1 with a conspicuous cruciform structure and head with complete longitudinal sutures (Fig. 82). Animal up to 40 mm or more long .... *Cryptops anomalans* (p. 52)

   NOTES:

   Tibial comb with 7-10 well spaced teeth (Fig. 83) and tarsal comb with 3-5 teeth on a slight ridge (Fig. 84). See Fig. 81 for position of combs.

   Almost all records are from urban/suburban areas.

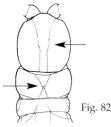

Fig. 82

Fig. 83

Fig. 84

- T1 without a cruciform suture, sutures on head (if visible) incomplete, generally at least slightly smaller than 40 mm ... 2

2. (1) Paired longitudinal sutures at posterior margin of head (Fig. 85). Tibial combs on last legs with 6-14 closely set teeth (Fig. 86) and tarsal comb with 4-9 teeth closely overlapping or fused together (Fig. 87). Five teeth in the centre of the labrum (Fig. 88). No ventral groove on prefemur of last legs ....
   .... *Cryptops parisi* (p. 54)

   NOTES:

   Anterior border of forcipular coxosternite relatively narrow and protuberant (Fig. 89).

   Often quite large, more than 30 mm.

   Mostly from synanthropic sites.

Fig. 85

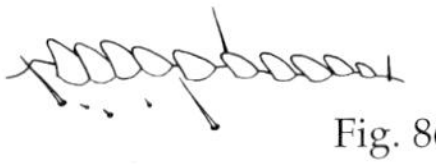

Fig. 86

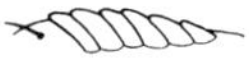

Fig. 87

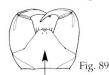

Fig. 88

Fig. 89

- No such sutures at posterior margin of head, only anterior ones (Fig. 90) and these may not be very distinct. Tibial comb of last legs with 5-8 teeth (Fig. 91) and tarsal comb with 2-4 distinctly separate teeth (Fig. 92) Three teeth in the centre of the labrum (Fig. 93). Distinct ventral groove on prefemur of last legs .... *Cryptops hortensis* (p. 53)

NOTES:

Anterior border of forcipular coxosternite is much less protuberant (Fig. 94).

The smallest and commonest of the three species; often found in non-synanthropic sites such as woodland as well as in gardens, etc.

C. anomalans is usually distinctly diagnosed by the cruciform suture on T1. The other two species, especially if immature, may not be so easy to separate but the characters of the last legs are valuable. Ultimately, examination of the labrum may be necessary. The teeth of this are relatively dark and usually visible in cleared animals or those with the mouthparts removed. Suspect any large specimens (over 25 mm) from synanthropic sites as being either *C. anomalans* or *C. parisi*.

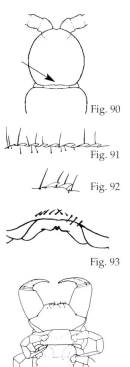

Fig. 90

Fig. 91

Fig. 92

Fig. 93

Fig. 94

A fourth species of *Cryptops* has been recorded from a tropical greenhouse in Cornwall and is identified as *C. doriae* Pocock (Lewis, 2007) (p. 54) whilst what appears to be a further species (J.G.E. Lewis, *pers.comm.*) is known from a heated greenhouse in South Wales. There are other species of *Cryptops* in other parts of Europe but it is unlikely that more than the three listed above (*C. anomalans, C. hortensis, C. parisi*) will be found in outdoor situations in Britain. The taxonomy of the genus outside the British Isles is confused with more than 130 species having been described at various times.

Scolopendromorpha also includes the so called 'giant centipedes' such as the *Scolopendra* species which occasionally come into Britain with imported goods. They are much larger than our native species, up to 15cm or more, frequently distinctively coloured. These animals have two ocelli on each side of the head and a forcipular coxosternite with projections bearing teeth a little like the arrangement in *Lithobius*. Such animals should be handled with care since their bite, although very unlikely to be fatal, may be extremely unpleasant and painful. There are several species in Southern Europe.

TABULAR KEY TO BRITISH SCOLOPENDROMORPHA (*CRYPTOPS* SPECIES)

Species	Maximum length	Head sutures	Tergite 1 sutures	Labrum
Cryptops anomalans	Up to 50 mm	Complete	Cruciform	Side pieces not notched
Cryptops hortensis	30 mm or less	Anterior only (short)	None distinct	Side pieces not notched (3 teeth)
Cryptops parisi	More than 30 mm	Anterior and posterior sutures	None distinct	Side pieces notched (5 teeth)

SPECIES NOTES

Cryptops anomalans (Plate 13, p. 96)

Maximum length:	Up to 50 mm, a large and impressive animal.
Head:	Longitudinal sutures complete, extending back from bases of antennae to posterior border of head.
Labrum:	Side pieces not notched at medial angles.
Forcipular coxosternite:	Anterior border slightly protuberant, two prominent short setae on each.
T1:	With a distinct cruciform suture, often enclosing a small area at its centre in the centre of the tergite and extending almost to the posterior border. May best be seen with the light at a slight angle and the specimen dry. A faint incomplete posterior transverse suture may be visible.
Last legs:	Cribriform area extends almost to the posterior border of the coxa, several smaller coxal setae among the pores. Prefemur usually without a distinct ventral groove. Tibial comb with 7-10 well spaced teeth. Tarsal comb with 3-5 teeth borne on a slight eminence (ridge).
Diagnostic features:	*C. anomalans* is distinguished by the characteristic T1 suture as well as those on the head, coxae, forcipular coxosternite border, tibial and tarsal combs, large size.
Distribution:	An animal mostly of synanthropic sites in the south-east and the west (including South Wales). Not yet recorded from Ireland.

Anterior border of forcipular coxosternite	Cribriform area of last legs	Prefemur of last leg	Tibial comb of last leg	Tarsal comb of last leg	Go to page
Slightly protuberant 2+2 short setae	Several smaller setae among pores	No distinct ventral groove	7-10 well spaced teeth	3-5 teeth on slight eminence	52
Barely protuberant 4+4 setae	Only one seta among pores	Distinct ventral groove	5-8 separate teeth	2-4 separate teeth	53
Narrow, protuberant about 4+4 setae	Several setae among pores	No distinct ventral groove	7-10 closely set teeth	4-6 closely overlapping or fused teeth	54

Cryptops hortensis (Plate 14, p. 96)

Maximum length:	30 mm, often much smaller.
Head:	Longitudinal sutures very incomplete, extending a short way back from the base of the antennae, absent posteriorly.
Labrum:	Side pieces not notched at medial angles.
Forcipular coxosternite:	Anterior border barely protuberant, about 4 setae on each side.
T1:	Without distinct sutures although an incomplete posterior transverse suture may be visible.
Last legs:	Cribriform area does not extend to posterior border of coxa, only one coxal seta among the pores. Prefemur with distinct ventral groove. Tibial comb with 6-14 closely set teeth. Tarsal comb with 4-9 closely overlapping teeth.
Diagnostic features:	Tibial and tarsal combs of last legs best, coxae of last legs, prefemoral groove on last legs, labrum (difficult to see without clearing or dissection), anterior border of forcipular coxosternite. *C. anomalans* is distinguished by T1 sutures, *C. parisi* may be more difficult sometimes.
Distribution:	A common animal of synanthropic sites, especially in the south but recorded from a wide variety of habitats there also including woodland. Essentially synanthropic in more northerly localities up to central Scotland. Ireland. Channel Islands.

Cryptops parisi (Plate 15, p. 96)

Maximum length:	30 mm or more, much larger than *C. hortensis* typically but not as large as the largest *C. anomalans*.
Head:	Longitudinal sutures incomplete, extending a short way back from the bases of the antennae and a short way forward posteriorly.
Labrum:	Side pieces notched at medial angles so that there appears to be five teeth in the centre of the labrum including the mid-piece.
Forcipular coxosternite:	Anterior border narrower and more protuberant than in the other species, about 4 setae on each side, rather stouter than in *C. hortensis*.
T1:	As in *C. hortensis*.
Last legs:	Cribriform area extends almost to the posterior border of the coxa, several coxal setae among the pores. Prefemur without a marked ventral groove. Tibial comb with 6-12 (rarely 13 or 14) closely set teeth. Tarsal comb with 4-8 (rarely 9) closely overlapping or even fused teeth.
Diagnostic features:	Tibial and tarsal combs of last legs best, coxae of last legs, labrum (difficult to see without clearing or dissection), anterior border of forcipular coxosternite. Distinguished from *C. anomalans* by T1 sutures, immatures (tibial and tarsal teeth fewer) can sometimes be quite difficult to distinguish from *C. hortensis*.
Distribution:	An animal of synanthropic sites, mostly in the south but it has been recorded from woodland in the south-west. Recorded as far north as Edinburgh and found in southern Ireland.

Cryptops doriae

Maximum length:	Up to 13 mm recorded for Cornish animals but foreign specimens may be much larger.
Head:	Without sutures.
Labrum:	Side pieces not notched.
Forcipular coxosternite:	Anterior border slightly curved on each side with slight median incision with 2-3 long and 2-3 short/medium length setae on each side.
T1:	Without sutures but in some specimens cleared in ethylene glycol, a fine anterior transverse groove or line, which is easily overlooked, is visible below the cuticle.
Last legs:	Femur with a single tooth. Tibial comb with about 8 teeth. Tarsal comb with 3-4 teeth.
Diagnostic features:	The tooth on the femur distinguishes from all other British species but is not always easy to see.
Distribution:	Recorded only from the Moist Tropical Biome at the Eden Project, Cornwall.

LITHOBIOMORPHA

Lithobiomorpha or 'stone centipedes' have only fifteen pairs of legs in the adult state and are usually some shade of brown or dark brown in colour (*Lithobius variegatus* is pale brown with variegated legs in the living state). These centipedes hatch from the egg with a reduced number of legs and go through a series of larval stages during which further legs are added at each moult until the full complement is present. They then pass through a series of post-larval stages until the adult stage is reached. During these stages of development the number of ocelli, teeth on forcipular coxosternite, coxal pores, etc. tend to show an increase in number up to the adult state. Adult lithobiomorphs vary in size between 5 mm (*Lamyetes caeculus*) and 35 mm or more (*Lithobius pilicornis*) so it should certainly not be assumed that small animals are young stages of larger ones.

The head is roughly heart shaped with a distinct ridge separated by a groove (sulcus) posteriorly and along half the sides from the main part of the head (Fig. 95). In some cases the shape of the head is distinctive (e.g. *Lithobius muticus* males, Fig. 127) and its width relative to the tergites affects the overall appearance of the animal. The antennae have from 18 to 50 articles and their number can be a valuable aid in the identification of species. Relative to the rest of the animal they represent about a third of the entire body length, less or more depending on species. Like head size this may affect the general appearance of the animal in the field.

The number and appearance of the ocelli (simple eyes) is characteristic of different species and varies from 0 (*Lamyctes caeculus*), 1 (*Lamyctes emarginatus*) or 3 (*Lithobius microps*, Fig. 115) to 30 or 40. These ocelli, which are blackish in colour and with a transparent lens, are on the antero-lateral side of the head capsule and are best seen in the dry state with the animal arranged at an angle. Characteristically the most posterior ocellus is larger than the others which lie in irregular rows or form a rosette. In front of and to the ventral side of the ocelli lies a pit-like sense organ of uncertain function, the organ of Tömösváry which resembles a small ocellus but is unpigmented and lacks the convex appearance of ocelli.

Fig. 95. Heart-shaped head of *Lamyctes emarginatus*.

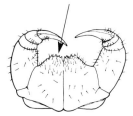

Fig. 96. Ventral view of coxosternite, showing teeth on anterior borders.

The forcipular segment has a rather short tergite with convex lateral borders. The coxosternite is broad at the base and with a well marked median cleft and prominent anterior borders (Fig. 96). These borders bear prominent, well-pigmented teeth, the arrangement and number of which is important in identification. In the descriptions that follow a formula such as 4 + 4 means that there are four on each side. Lateral to the teeth in *Lithobius* there is a distinct short spine, the paradontal spine.

There are fifteen trunk segments in both sexes. Characteristic of them are alternate large and short tergites along the back. The two large ones together (T7, T8) makes identification of the others easier (Fig. 97). T7, T9, T11 and T13 may have rounded posterior angles, right angles or distinct posterior projections. The presence or absence and shape of such posterior tergite projections is important in identification.

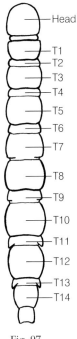

Fig. 97.

All the legs comprise a coxa and six articles. In some species such as *Lithobius crassipes* the tarsus and metatarsus are fused together on legs 1 to 11. The legs of all species bear hairs or setae and in *Lithobius* but not *Lamyctes* there are distinct strong spines at the distal ends of the articles (except the metatarsus). The presence or absence of given spines and their presence on particular legs is of systematic importance. An explanation of the terminology used for the spines is given in the box opposite and is shown in Figs 98 and 99. The only spines that generally need to be considered here are 15VaC (coxolateral spine), 15VmC and the accessory spine between 15VpP and DpP. It is important to note that the small spine referred to as VaC is ventro-lateral and only occurs in a few species whereas there is another small spine, DaC dorso-laterally which is common

Characters to look for in identification include the forcipular coxosternite teeth, the appearance of the tergites (projections), claw of last leg, antennal articles and possibly 15VaC or ocelli. Some lithobiids can be quite tricky in some cases especially if damaged or immature.

Dichotomous (p. 58) and tabular keys (p. 68) are given.

A note on Spinulation

• Legs are numbered 1-15 from front to back.

• Each may have spines dorsally (upper surface) (D) and ventrally (lower surface) (V).

• If the maximum number at any position is 3; these may be referred to as anterior (a), median (m – usually larger than the other two) and posterior (inner) (p).

• Spines can occur on the coxa (C), trochanter (t), prefemur (P), femur (F) or tarsus (T).

So the formula 15VaC is made up from

Leg number:	1-15
Dorsal or ventral:	D or V
Anterior (outer), median or posterior (inner):	a, m or p
Coxa, trochanter, prefemur, femur, tarsus:	C, t, P, F or T

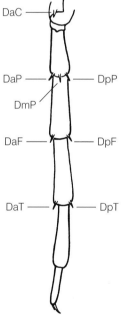
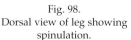
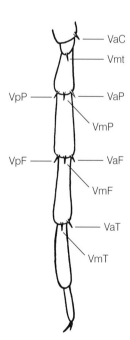

Fig. 98.
Dorsal view of leg showing spinulation.

Fig. 99.
Ventral view of leg showing spinulation (VmC not shown).

KEYS TO BRITISH LITHOBIOMORPHA

1. Only one ocellus on each side of the head (Fig. 100) or ocelli absent, no projections to any of the tergites, no spines (only setae/bristles) on the legs (Fig. 101), forcipular coxosternite with 3 + 3 teeth (Fig. 102), claws of last legs triple (Fig. 103), always female. Variable in colour from very light brown to very dark or greyish .... Henicopidae: *Lamyctes* species (p. 58)

- At least three ocelli on each side, with or without projections on tergites, at least some spines present on some of the legs (but see note under *Lithobius microps*, p. 77), forcipular coxosternite with 2 + 2 to 6 + 6 or more teeth, claws of last legs single or double, never triple, males or females. Variable in colour ....
.... Lithobiidae: *Lithobius* species (p. 59)

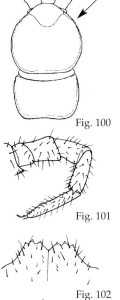

Fig. 100

Fig. 101

Fig. 102

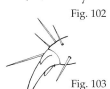

Fig. 103

HENICOPIDAE

1. One distinct ocellus on each side of the head (Fig. 100), colour chestnut brown to dark brown or sometimes greyish, up to 10.5 mm .... *Lamyctes emarginatus* (p. 70)

NOTE: An outdoor species, commonest in late summer and autumn.

- Ocelli completely absent but the organ of Tömösváry is relatively dark and conspicuous, colour pale yellowish with extremities and bases of antennae orange, up to 5 mm long ....
.... *Lamyctes caeculus* (p. 70)

NOTE: Only known as a hothouse species in northern Europe.

LITHOBIIDAE

Lithobius species in Britain can be conveniently divided into relatively large forms (up to 30 mm or more) with 4-7 or more teeth on each forcipular coxosternite: *L. variegatus*, *L. forficatus*, *L. peregrinus*, *L. piceus* (sometimes only 3), *L. pilicornis* and the remaining, generally smaller species (up to 17 mm or more in *L. melanops* but often less than 15 mm) with 2 (rarely 3) teeth on each side.

However, very young specimens of *Lithobius piceus* may have only two teeth on the forcipular coxosternite in which case they could key out in the area of *Lithobius macilentus / melanops / borealis*. In *Lithobius lucifugus*, animals from elsewhere in Europe have been very rarely recorded with 4+4 teeth and would probably key out as *L. pilicornis* although there are no projections on T9, T11 or T13.

KEY TO THE BRITISH SPECIES OF *LITHOBIUS*

1. Forcipular coxosternite with 4 or more teeth on each side (Fig. 104); possibly fewer in immature animals. Distinct posterior projections on tergites T11 and T13 (Fig. 105); may also be present on T9 or on T7 and T9). Relatively large animals when mature (20-40 mm) 2

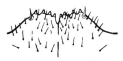

Fig. 104

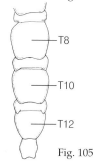

Fig. 105

- Forcipular coxosternite with two teeth on each side (Fig. 106). Projections on tergites T9, T11 or T13 present or absent. Relatively smaller when mature (<17 mm) 6

   NOTE: *Lithobius piceus* may have 3 + 3 coxosternite teeth in immature animals. Correspondingly, some species such as *Lithobius melanops* or *Lithobius crassipes* which normally have 2 + 2 occasionally have 2 + 3 or 3 + 3.

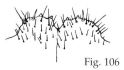

Fig. 106

2 (1) No projections on tergite T9, claw of 15th leg single or with vestigial accessory claw, female gonopods with 2 + 2 conical spurs. Spines 15VaC and 15VmC present (Fig. 107) ....
.... *Lithobius pilicornis* (p. 79)

   NOTE: May be very large (up to 40 mm). South-western or in urban sites.

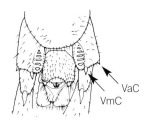

Fig. 107

- Projections on tergite T9 obvious (Fig. 105), claw of 15th leg double or single, female gonopod may have more than 2 + 2 spurs. 15VaC may be present but 15VmC is always absent ... 3

3 (2) Claw of 15th legs single, spine 15VaC (and 15 VmC) absent, female gonopod spurs 2 + 2 normally (Fig. 108) 4

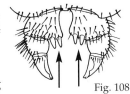

Fig. 108

NOTE: Common and widespread animals.

-        Claw of 11th leg with an accessory claw and so appearing double, spine 15VaC present (see Fig. 107; 15 VmC absent), female gonopod spurs 2 + 2 or more 5

4 (3) Projections present on T7 (Fig. 109), coxal pores on last legs round (Fig. 110), very conspicuous variegations on legs of living or freshly dead animals .... *Lithobius variegatus* (p. 81)

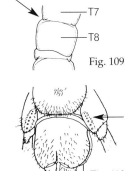

Fig. 109

NOTE: Widespread and common in much of Britain except the eastern side; tends not to be found in urban areas.

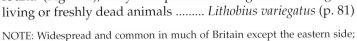

Fig. 110

-        No projections on tergite T7 (Fig. 111), coxal pores oval or slit shaped (Fig. 112), no conspicuous variegations but a more or less uniform chestnut brown .... *Lithobius forficatus* (p. 74)

Fig. 111

NOTE: Very common, especially in human influenced habitats; the common large brown lithobiid of most of Britain.

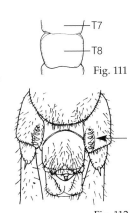

Fig. 112

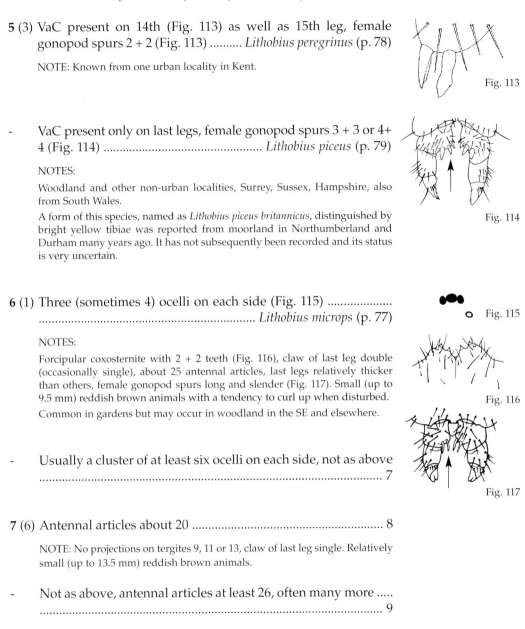

5 (3) VaC present on 14th (Fig. 113) as well as 15th leg, female gonopod spurs 2 + 2 (Fig. 113) .... *Lithobius peregrinus* (p. 78)

NOTE: Known from one urban locality in Kent.

Fig. 113

- VaC present only on last legs, female gonopod spurs 3 + 3 or 4+ 4 (Fig. 114) .... *Lithobius piceus* (p. 79)

NOTES:

Woodland and other non-urban localities, Surrey, Sussex, Hampshire, also from South Wales.

A form of this species, named as *Lithobius piceus britannicus*, distinguished by bright yellow tibiae was reported from moorland in Northumberland and Durham many years ago. It has not subsequently been recorded and its status is very uncertain.

Fig. 114

6 (1) Three (sometimes 4) ocelli on each side (Fig. 115) ....
.... *Lithobius microps* (p. 77)

Fig. 115

NOTES:

Forcipular coxosternite with 2 + 2 teeth (Fig. 116), claw of last leg double (occasionally single), about 25 antennal articles, last legs relatively thicker than others, female gonopod spurs long and slender (Fig. 117). Small (up to 9.5 mm) reddish brown animals with a tendency to curl up when disturbed.

Common in gardens but may occur in woodland in the SE and elsewhere.

Fig. 116

- Usually a cluster of at least six ocelli on each side, not as above 7

Fig. 117

7 (6) Antennal articles about 20 8

NOTE: No projections on tergites 9, 11 or 13, claw of last leg single. Relatively small (up to 13.5 mm) reddish brown animals.

- Not as above, antennal articles at least 26, often many more .....
.... 9

8 (7) Up to 13.5 mm, ocelli 9-13 with posterior slightly larger than others which are arranged in 2-3 straight rows (Fig. 118). Forcipular coxosternite without definite shoulders, outer teeth project further forward than inner (Fig. 119); 3 + 3 teeth sometimes occur. No distinctive features on tibia of last leg of male (Fig. 120) .... *Lithobius crassipes* (p. 72)

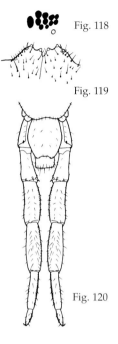

Fig. 118

Fig. 119

Fig. 120

NOTES:

Can be difficult to separate from *L. curtipes*, see NOTES below.

Very common in much of northern and eastern Britain; seems to be absent in Devon and Cornwall.

\- Up to 11 mm, ocelli 6-9 with two relatively large posterior ones and others not in definite rows – often an incomplete rosette (Fig. 121). Forcipular coxosternite with two closely set teeth projecting forward to about the same extent (Fig. 122). Male has a distinct flattened projection on the postero-lateral extremity of the tibia of the last leg (Fig. 123) ....
.... *Lithobius curtipes* (p. 73)

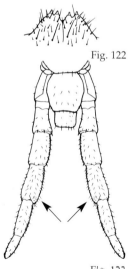

Fig. 121

Fig. 122

Fig. 123

NOTES:

Scattered records from across England and Wales except the far south-west.

These two species can be difficult to separate unless there are males present. *L. curtipes* has a much more pronounced tendency to curl up when disturbed (as with *L. microps*) than *L. crassipes*; the shape of the forcipular coxosternite and the arrangement of the ocelli are useful pointers. *L. curtipes* has so far not been recorded from Scotland or Ireland and there may well be distinctive differences in their ecology. Refer to species notes.

9 (7) No projections on tergites 9, 11 or 13, antennal articles at least 34. Often rather darkish or black animals up to 15 mm long 10

- Projections on at least tergites 11 and 13 or 13 alone. Chestnut brown, light brown or occasionally dark chestnut; up to 17 mm long 12

10 (9) Double claw on 15th legs, head about as broad as long, little broader than the 3rd tergite (Fig. 124), ocelli 9-11 on each side: two relatively large posteriorly and the remainder forming a rosette (Fig. 125). Males with very distinct postero-lateral projection on femur (4th article from end) of 15th leg (Fig. 126) .... *Lithobius calcaratus* (p. 72)

NOTES:

Generally an animal of moorland, heath and grassland; has also been found in the splash zone of maritime locations. Often found in rather dry locations.

L. lapidicola in which the projections on T13 may appear to be more or less absent may also key out here. The 15th leg of this species has a double claw.

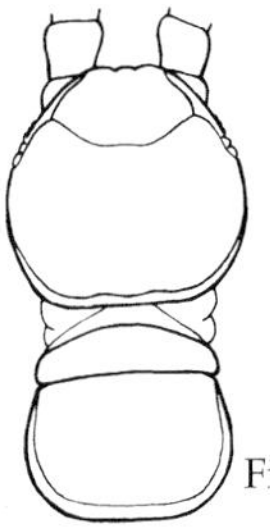

Fig. 124

Fig. 125

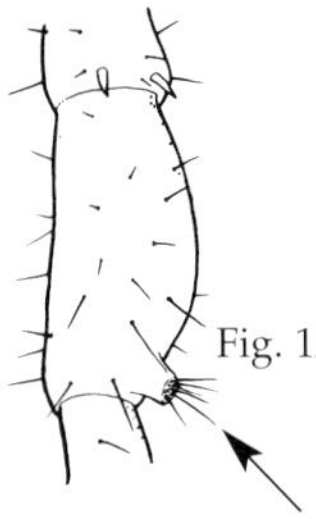

Fig. 126

- Single claw on 15th legs, ocelli with one large then several rows of smaller ones. Males lack the projection on the 15th leg 11

11 (10) Head markedly broad compared with the rest of the body, especially in the male where it is 1.25 times as broad as long (Fig. 127), ocelli 10-14; one large, others in three or four rows (Fig. 128). Small, indistinct swelling on dorsal surface of tibia of 14th leg in males (Fig. 129) ....
.... *Lithobius muticus* (p. 77)

NOTE: Characteristically an animal of deciduous woodland in SE England but occasionally found elsewhere.

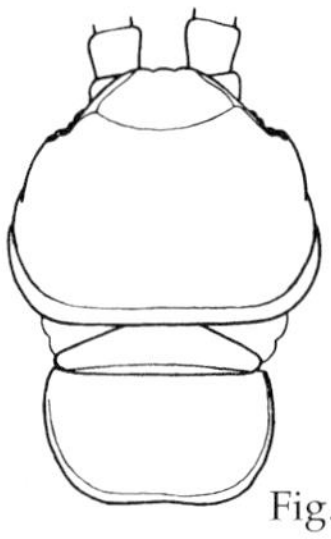

Fig. 127

Fig. 128

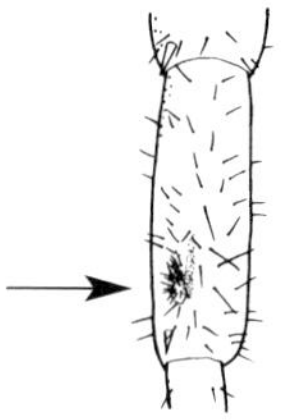

Fig. 129

- Head not markedly broader than rest of body (Fig. 130); ocelli 13-23 with 4-6 curved rows (Fig. 131). No such swelling on male 14th tibia .... *Lithobius lucifugus* (p. 75)

NOTE: Recorded from an urban area in Edinburgh and a greenhouse on Mull but usually described as an alpine species.

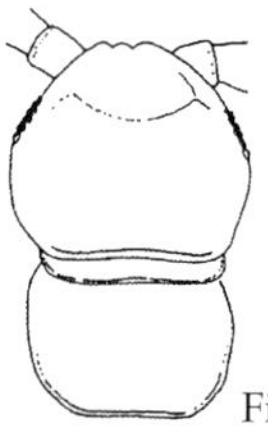

Fig. 130

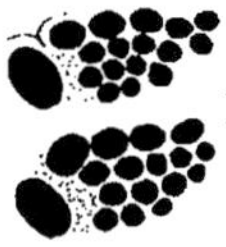

Fig. 131

12 (9) Claw of 15th legs single (Fig. 132), ocelli 14-18 ....
.... *Lithobius tenebrosus* (p. 80)

NOTES:

Antennal articles 36-43 (Fig. 133), up to 14 mm long.

Only recent record is from a Welsh coastal site but older ones are from Cornwall and Durham.

Fig. 132

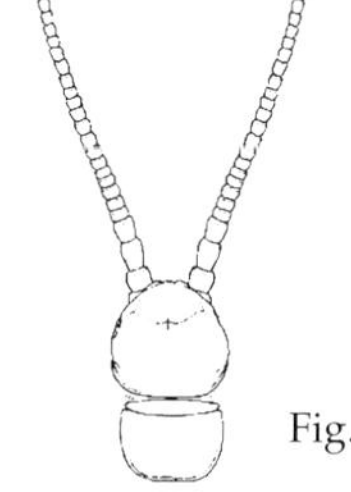

Fig. 133

- Claw of 15th legs double, ocelli 7-13 13

13 (12) Tergite T9 with distinct, broad projections, also on T11 and T13 (Fig. 134) 14

- No projections on tergite T9, sometimes only on T13 or poorly developed on T11 17

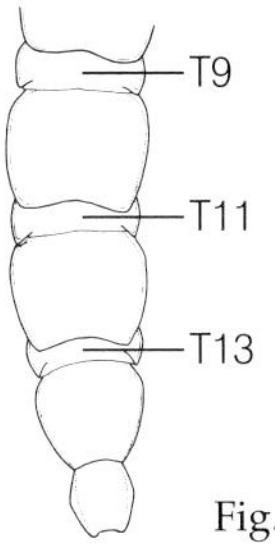

Fig. 134

14 (13) Forcipular coxosternite teeth with median ones projecting further forward than lateral and no shoulders lateral to these teeth (Fig. 135). Very prominent projections on tergites T9, T11, T13 (Fig. 136) .... *Lithobius macilentus* (p. 76)

NOTES:

Chestnut brown in colour; all British specimens appear to be female.

Widespread but scattered across Britain.

Fig. 135

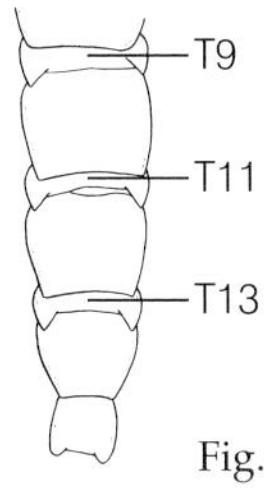

Fig. 136

- Median teeth of forcipular coxosternite less forward than lateral, more or less distinct shoulders laterally (Fig. 137). Rather broad projections on tergite T9 (Fig. 134) 15

NOTE: Males and females both found in Britain.

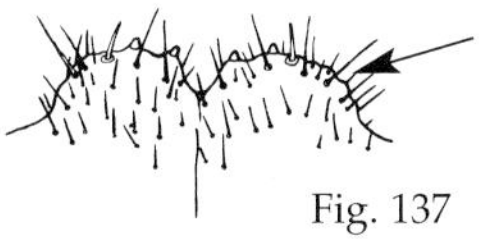

Fig. 137

15 (14) Accessory spine between VpP and DpP on 15th leg (Fig. 138) .... Northern specimens of *Lithobius borealis* (p. 71)

NOTES:

Some northern specimens of this species have broad projections on T9 approaching those of *L. melanops* in which case the accessory spine is critical.

Careful examination of the spine series on the prefemur will show this 'extra' spine; normally there are three ventral spines (VaP, VmP, VpP) and two or three dorsal ones (DmP, DpP and sometimes DaP) with the accessory one between the posterior ones VpP and DpP.

Mountains, moorland and lowland sites, especially in western Britain; widespread.

Fig. 138

- No such accessory spine 16

16 (15) Females with 2 + 2 gonopod spurs (Fig. 139), spine 15VaC absent, definite shoulders to forcipular coxosternite (Fig. 140). Usually lightish brown with a distinct broad median band in life .... *Lithobius melanops* (p. 76)

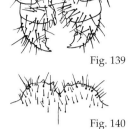

Fig. 139

Fig. 140

NOTES:

Rarely additional gonopod spurs may be seen females.

Widespread, often associated with human activity (including gardens) or in coastal sites.

\-   Females with 3 + 3 gonopod spurs (Fig. 141), spine 15VaC may be present, no definite shoulders to forcipular coxosternite (Fig. 142). Variable but more or less uniform chestnut brown in colour and lacking the median darker band of *L. melanops* .... *Lithobius tricuspis* (p. 80)

Fig. 141

Fig. 142

NOTES:

Some Continental specimens of *L. tricuspis* have only a single claw on the last leg; possibly this condition could be found in British examples in which case it would key out at couplet 12.

Various habitats. Quite widespread in parts of South Devon, but has occurred in the Isle of Wight and South Wales.

17 (13) Tergite T9 without projections (Fig. 143; may be present in northern specimens) but projections present on tergites T11 and T13. Forcipular coxosternite has well developed shoulders as in *L. melanops* (Fig. 144), accessory spine on prefemur of 15th legs between VpP and DpP (Fig. 145). Up to 12.5 mm .... *Lithobius borealis* (p. 71)

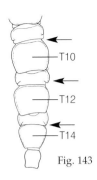

—T10

—T12

—T14

Fig. 143

NOTES:

Some northern specimens of this species have broad projections on T9 approaching those of *L. melanops* in which case the accessory spine is critical.

Fig. 144

Careful examination of the spine series on the prefemur will show this 'extra' spine; normally there are three ventral spines (VaP, VmP, VpP) and two or three dorsal ones (DmP, DpP and sometimes DaP) with the accessory one between the posterior ones VpP and DpP.

Mountains, moorland and lowland sites, especially in western Britain; widespread.

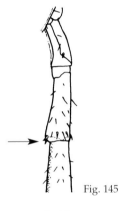

Fig. 145

—   Tergite T9 without projections (may also be absent on T11 and possibly T13). Shoulders of forcipular coxosternite weakly developed (Fig. 146), tergites described as 'wrinkled', no accessory spine on 15th legs, up to 8 mm long .... *Lithobius lapidicola* (p. 74)

Fig. 146

NOTES:

Recorded from the Kent and Suffolk coasts and from glasshouses elsewhere.

Possibly more widespread but overlooked.

Tabular Key to British Lithobiomorpha

Species	Size (mm)	Antennal articles	Ocelli	Forcipular teeth (pairs)	Claw of 15th leg	Coxal pores shape
Lithobius						
L. variegatus	24	35-46	13-18	6-7	single	round
L. forficatus	30	35-43	20-30	5-7	single	oval/slit
L. peregrinus	24	38-52	11-19	5-7	double	round/slit
L. piceus	21	49-54	11-16	3-5	double	round
L. pilicornis	35	29-34	20-40	3-6	single	oval/slit
L. melanops	17	32-42	10-13	2-(3)	double	round
L. tricuspis	14	40-45	10-12	2	double	round
L. borealis	12.5	28-34	8-12	2	double	round
L. lapidicola	8	26-34	10-11	2	double	round
L. macilentus	14	39-45	7-9	2	double	round
L. tenebrosus	14	36-43	14-18	2	single	round
L. calcaratus	15	39-50	7-9	2	double	round
L. muticus	15	34-43	10-14	2-(3)	single	round
L. lucifugus	17	33-50	13-23	2-(4)	single	round
L. crassipes	13.5	20	9-13	2	single	round
L. curtipes	11	20	6-9	2	single	round
L. microps	9.5	23-27	3(-4)	2	double (single)	round
Lamyctes						
L. emarginatus	10.5	25	1	3	triple	round
L. caeculus	5	24	0	3	triple	round

NB: Immatures may only have 3+3 forcipular sternite teeth in some cases; other characters may need to be checked

Tergite projections				15VaC	Female gonopod spurs	Other notable features	Go to page
✔	✔	✔	✔		2	Legs with banding	81
	✔	✔	✔		2		74
	✔	✔	✔	✔	2	14VaC, 15VaC	78
	✔	✔	✔	✔	3-4	15VaC	79
		✔	✔	✔	2	15VmC, 15VaC	79
	✔	✔	✔		2	Colour	76
	✔	✔	✔	(✔)	3		80
(✔)	✔	✔			2	Accessory spine on leg 15	71
		(✔)	(✔)		2		74
	✔	✔	✔		2	Shape of forcipular coxosternite, all females	76
	✔	✔	✔		2	1 recent Welsh site	80
					2	Male 15th leg, colour	72
					2-3	Male 14th leg and head shape	77
					2	1 Scottish site	75
					2		72
					2	Male 15th leg, ocelli	73
					2	3 ocelli each side	77
					2	Spines absent, all females	70
					2	Hothouse species	70

Species notes

Henicopidae

Lamyctes caeculus

Maximum length:	5 mm.
Colour:	Yellow or pale orange-brown with extremities and bases of antennae orange.
Head:	As broad as T3.
Antennae:	About one quarter of body length, 24 articles.
Ocelli:	Absent; organ of Tömösváry conspicuous.
Forcipular coxosternite:	3 + 3 teeth (sometimes 4 + 4), lateral ones much smaller and less projecting than others.
Tergites:	No prominent projections, angles rounded or right angled.
Coxal pores:	Round, relatively large, 2-3 on each coxa.
Legs:	No spines such as those found on *Lithobius* species are present, only setae. Claw of 15th leg triple.
Males:	Not known in Britain.
Female genitalia:	Similar to *L. emarginatus*.
Diagnostic features:	Forcipular coxosternite teeth, absence of ocelli, complete lack of leg spines, claw of last legs, all females.
Distribution:	Recorded from the Eden Project in Cornwall (Moist Tropical Biome) & The National Botanic Garden of Wales glasshouse.

Lamyctes emarginatus

Maximum length:	10.5 mm.
Colour:	Chestnut brown to dark brown.
Head:	As broad as long or broader, almost as broad as T3.
Antennae:	One third to two fifths of body length, usually 25 articles.
Ocelli:	One only on each side.
Forcipular coxosternite:	3 + 3 teeth, lateral ones much smaller and less projecting than others.
Tergites:	No prominent projections.
Coxal pores:	Round, 2-3 on each coxa.
Legs:	No spines such as those found on *Lithobius* species are present, only setae. Claw of 15th leg triple.
Males:	Not known in Britain.

Female genitalia:	Two conical spurs, claw without denticles.
Diagnostic features:	Forcipular coxosternite teeth, ocelli, complete lack of leg spines, claw of last legs, all females.
Distribution:	Often found in cultivated areas and in relatively wet habitats but also found on acid heath/moorland, etc. Scattered records from across England, Wales and Scotland to the Shetlands. Ireland.

LITHOBIIDAE

Lithobius borealis

Maximum length:	12.5 mm.
Colour:	Chestnut brown to dark brown.
Head:	About as broad as long, almost as broad as T5.
Antennae:	About two fifths body length; 28-34 articles.
Ocelli:	8-12 on each side, posterior much larger than others which are arranged in about three fairly regular rows.
Forcipular coxosternite:	2 + 2 with rather prominent shoulders, similar to *L. melanops*.
Tergites:	Posterior angles of T9 usually right angled but in northern specimens often have fairly prominent projections. T11 and T13 with clear projections, rather blunt on T11.
Coxal pores:	Round, 2 to 5 on each coxa.
Legs:	An accessory spine between the ventral VpP and the dorsal DpP on the prefemur of the last legs is characteristic. Claw of 15th leg double.
Males:	No specific secondary sexual characteristics.
Female genitalia:	2 conical spurs on each side, claw with large dorsal denticle and slightly smaller ventral one placed more proximally.
Diagnostic features:	Forcipular coxosternite, tergites, accessory spine on last leg. May be difficult to separate from *L. melanops* if it has projections on T9. Check for the accessory spine on the last leg.
Distribution:	Characteristic of much moor and heath in the western part of Britain, woodland, scrub, arable, etc. Not usually found in urban areas.

This is *L. borealis* Meinert, formerly referred to as *L. lapidicola* Latzel and called *L. lapidicola* Meinert in some earlier British texts including that of Eason (1964). *L. lapidicola* Meinert 1872 is another species, known also as *L. pusillus* and is described elsewhere in this account.

Lithobius calcaratus (Plate 9, p. 95)

Maximum length:	15 mm.
Colour:	Dark brown to almost black, sometimes greyish.
Head:	As broad as long, a little broader than T5.
Antennae:	About two fifths of body length, 39 - 50 articles.
Ocelli:	7-9; a relatively small posterior ocellus immediately preceded by a larger intermediate one and then a rosette of 7.
Forcipular coxosternite:	2 + 2 teeth, sloping, irregular shoulders.
Tergites:	No projections on T9, T11 or T13.
Coxal pores:	Round, 2-4 on each coxa.
Legs:	Claw of 15th leg double.
Males:	Femur of 15th leg very swollen and protuberant along dorsal border. A characteristic wart-like process surmounted by a tuft of setae projects backwards from the dorsal surface of this.
Female genitalia:	2 conical spurs on each side, claw with small but distinct dorsal denticle but usually no ventral one.
Diagnostic features:	Shiny black, fast running specimens from dry sites are usually this species. The colour is distinct, but shared with *L. muticus* (which has a single claw on leg 15) and some *L. borealis*. Forcipular coxosternite, antennae, ocelli, tergites, double claw on last legs. Mature males quite distinctive. A fast moving animal, often difficult to capture.
Distribution:	Very much a rural animal, often found in dry grassland both alkaline and acid and on moorland and sometimes above the seashore. England, Wales and southern Scotland. Not recorded from Ireland.

Lithobius crassipes

Maximum length:	13.5 mm.
Colour:	Chestnut brown.
Head:	Usually a little broader than long, broader than T3 but narrower than T5.
Antennae:	Less than one third body length; 18-21 (usually 20) articles.
Ocelli:	9-13, posterior slightly larger than others which are arranged in 2-3 fairly straight rows.
Forcipular coxosternite:	2 + 2 teeth (rarely more, even up to 3 + 4), lateral project slightly further forward than medial, no definite shoulders.
Tergites:	No trace of lobes or projections on T9, T11 or T13.
Coxal pores:	Round, 2-4 on each coxa.

Legs:	Tarsus and metatarsus fused on legs 1-11. 14th and 15th legs rather thickened in both sexes. Claw of 15th leg single.
Males:	No specific secondary sexual structures.
Female genitalia:	2 conical spurs on each side. Claw with a large dorsal denticle and a slightly smaller ventral one.
Diagnostic features:	Antennae, tergites, forcipular coxosternite, ocelli. May not be always easy to separate from *L. curtipes*.
Distribution:	Woodland, grassland, arable, heath and moorland, etc. Relatively rarely found in urban sites. Has a marked eastern bias in southern England and is the common small rural lithobiid of many areas of Britain. Probably more or less absent in Devon and Cornwall. Some Irish records.

Lithobius curtipes (Plate 10, p. 95)

Maximum length:	11 mm.
Colour:	Chestnut brown.
Head:	As broad as long, broader than T3 but narrower than T5.
Antennae:	One third to two fifths body length, 19-20 articles.
Ocelli:	6-9, usual arrangement is a relatively small posterior ocellus, a larger intermediate one and then a rosette (incomplete ventrally) of 5 ocelli surrounding a central one.
Forcipular coxosternite:	Anterior border rather narrow with 2 + 2 rather closely set teeth more or less all reaching the same level with the lateral pair most prominent.
Tergites:	No projections on T9, T11 or T13.
Coxal pores:	Round, 2-4 on each coxa.
Legs:	Tarsus and metatarsus fused on legs 1 to 11. 14th and 15th legs rather thickened in both sexes, more so in male. Claw of 15th leg single.
Males:	Tibia of 15th leg has a flattened projection on posterodorsal extremity.
Female genitalia:	2 conical spurs on each side. Claw with well developed dorsal denticle and smaller ventral.
Diagnostic features:	A species that is not always easy to distinguish from *L. crassipes* unless males are present. Ocelli, forcipular coxosternite, male 15th leg, spinulation. Tends to curl up when disturbed, a characteristic shared with *L. microps*.
Distribution:	Scattered records from across England and Wales, many are from woodland (including ancient woodland) but has also been recorded from limestone grassland in Wales. Possibly under-recorded because of confusion with the apparently commoner *L. crassipes*. Not known from Devon and Cornwall or from Scotland and Ireland.

Lithobius forficatus

Maximum length:	30 mm.
Colour:	Chestnut brown (freshly moulted individuals are pale blue).
Head:	A little broader than long, usually about as broad as T3.
Antennae:	Up to one third of body length, 35-43 articles.
Ocelli:	20 to 30 on each side, posterior much larger than any others, others arranged in 5 or 6 irregular rows.
Forcipular coxosternite:	Anterior border less prominent and relatively narrower than *L. variegatus*. 5 + 5 to 6 + 7 teeth. Immatures with fewer.
Tergites:	T9, T11 and T13 with prominent projections.
Coxal pores:	Oval or slit shaped (in larger specimens), 5-9 on each coxa.
Legs:	Much stouter than in *L. variegatus*. 15th leg with single claw.
Males:	No distinctive secondary sexual characteristics.
Female genitalia:	2 conical spurs, occasionally a third on one side only. Claw of gonopod with distinct dorsal and lateral denticles.
Diagnostic features:	The only common large brown lithobiid in most areas although *L. pilicornis* may take its place where that species occurs. Forcipular coxosternite, tergites, no coxolateral spine (VaC) on last leg. Claw of 15th leg single.
Distribution:	Widespread in urban and suburban areas and common in many rural ones. Sometimes found inside houses. All over Britain and Ireland. Channel Islands.

Lithobius lapidicola

Maximum length:	8 mm or more.
Colour:	Chestnut brown.
Antennae:	One third of body length, 26-34 articles.
Ocelli:	Up to 11, posterior ocellus usually a little larger than next largest; others in 3-4 irregular rows.
Forcipular coxosternite:	2 + 2 teeth, internal slightly further forward than lateral. Laterally sides slope backwards forming at most feeble shoulders.
Tergites:	Wrinkling of T5 backwards is described as characteristic of the species. T9 obtuse or square, T11 square or with trace of projections, T13 with trace of or more or less clear projections.
Coxal pores:	Round, 2-5 on each coxa.
Legs:	15th leg with double claw.
Males:	No specific secondary sexual characteristics.

Female genitalia:	Two conical spurs on each side, claw with small distal medial denticle and smaller more proximal lateral one.
Diagnostic features:	Lack of accessory spine on 15th leg distinguishes from *L. borealis*. It lacks the swollen last two pairs of legs characteristic of the comparably small *L. microps* (and has more ocelli). It may key out as *L. calcaratus* but is quite different in appearance and lacks the projection on the 15th leg of males.
Distribution:	Recorded outdoors from eastern coastal sites (Kent, Suffolk) and glasshouses in Edinburgh and Dorset. May well be under-recorded.

This is not the *L. lapidicola* of earlier British works which is now known as *L. borealis*.

Lithobius lucifugus

Maximum length:	17 mm.
Colour:	Light brown, reddish brown in centre of head and in a wide dorsomedian stripe.
Antennae:	Short, not more than two fifths of body length, 33-50 articles.
Ocelli:	13-23, one posterior plus 4 to 6 rows.
Forcipular coxosternite:	2 + 2 conical teeth (very variable, 4 + 4 is recorded in some European specimens). Sides slope backwards without well developed shoulders.
Tergites:	No projections on T9, T11, T13.
Coxal pores:	More or less round, 4-7 on each coxa but additional much smaller pores may also be present.
Legs:	15th leg has single claw.
Males:	15th leg slightly thickened but without any special structures.
Female genitalia:	2 cylindro-conical spurs on each side, claws tridentate (i.e. well developed dorsal and ventral denticles).
Diagnostic features:	Combination of features above. It could key out as *L. muticus* but lacks the feature of the 14th leg of males of that species.
Distribution:	Recorded from a kirk-yard in Edinburgh and from a greenhouse on Mull.

Often described as a species of alpine situations in Europe; presumably introduced to these Scottish sites.

Lithobius macilentus

Maximum length:	14 mm.
Colour:	Chestnut brown.
Head:	A little broader than long, almost as broad as T5.
Antennae:	Two fifths to a half body length, 39-45 articles.
Ocelli:	7-9, posterior much the same size as the others which are arranged in a rather irregular rosette.
Forcipular coxosternite:	2 + 2 rather small pointed, widely spaced teeth with the medial pair pointing further forward than the lateral ones. No shoulders.
Tergites:	T9, T11 and T13 with prominent projections.
Coxal pores:	Round, 4-5 on each coxa.
Legs:	Claw of 15th leg double.
Males:	Not known in Britain.
Female genitalia:	2 conical spurs, claw with small dorsal denticle and an even smaller ventral one.
Diagnostic features:	Forcipular coxosternite, tergites, claw of last legs, all females.
Distribution:	Typically a rural woodland animal but known from other types of habitat. Scattered records from across England, Wales and southern Scotland. Not recorded from the South-West or Ireland.

Referred to as *L. aulacopus* in Eason (1964).

Lithobius melanops

Maximum length:	17 mm.
Colour:	Chestnut brown. In life a darker median streak is often visible on a mid-brown background.
Head:	As long as broad, as broad as T3 or a little broader.
Antennae:	About two fifths of body length, 32-42 articles.
Ocelli:	10-13. Posterior much larger than others which are in about 3 curved rows.
Forcipular coxosternite:	2 + 2 teeth, rarely an extra one, prominent lateral shoulders.
Tergites:	T9 with broad, rather blunt projections, T11 and T13 with prominent projections.
Coxal pores:	Round, 3-6 on each coxa.
Legs:	15th legs with double claw.
Males:	No specific secondary sexual structures.

Female genitalia:	Two conical spurs on each gonopod, sometimes an extra on one side. Claw with a large dorsal and a slightly smaller ventral denticle.
Diagnostic features:	Forcipular coxosternite, tergites, double claw on 15th leg, no accessory spine or coxolateral spine (VaC) on that leg.
Distribution:	Common in urban sites and occurring inside houses but also an animal of coastal sites and sand dunes.

Throughout Britain (to Shetlands) and Ireland.

Lithobius microps

Maximum length:	9.5 mm.
Colour:	Chestnut brown (often quite light).
Head:	About as broad as long, about as broad as T3.
Antennae:	Usually rather less than one third body length, 23-27 (usually 25) articles.
Ocelli:	3 (rarely 4) in a single row (if 4 then extra one is just above).
Forcipular coxosternite:	2 + 2 pointed teeth, lateral pair relatively far forward. Sometimes feeble shoulders laterally.
Tergites:	No projections on T9, T11, T13.
Coxal pores:	Round, 1-4 on each coxa.
Legs:	14th and 15th markedly thickened in both sexes. Claw of last leg double (sometimes single).
Males:	No specific secondary sexual characters.
Female genitalia:	Two rather long slender spurs, claw with large dorsal and smaller ventral denticle.
Diagnostic features:	Ocelli, forcipular coxosternite, tergites, female gonopod spurs, small size and tendency to curl up when disturbed.
Distribution:	Very much an animal of synanthropic sites but also found in woodland in the south. England and Wales.

Formerly known as *L. duboscqui*, this is the *L. microps* of Meinert, 1868. Animals with a single claw on the 15th legs have been called var. *fosteri*. Animals without any leg spines have been found in mid-north Wales and are referred to as var. *exarmatus*.

Lithobius muticus (Plate 11, p. 95)

Maximum length:	15 mm.
Colour:	Dark brown.
Head:	In males very broad, about 1.25 times length and wider than T10. In females only slightly broader than long, about as broad as T5.
Antennae:	Two fifths to a half body length, 34-43 articles.

Ocelli:	10-14. Posterior only slightly larger than any of the others which form 3-4 rows in a roughly triangular mass.
Forcipular coxosternite:	2 + 2 teeth (sometimes 3 + 3), sloping irregular lateral shoulders.
Tergites:	No conspicuous projections on T9, T11, T13 but T11 and T13 may have very slightly projecting lobes.
Coxal pores:	Round, 3-6 on each coxa.
Legs:	14th and 15th somewhat thickened in both sexes. Claw of 15th leg single.
Males:	Tibia of 14th leg bears small indistinct swelling topped with a tuft of setae just before the spine DpT.
Female genitalia:	Two or three conical spurs, claw with a small dorsal and even smaller ventral denticle.
Diagnostic features	Colour, shape and size of head in male, forcipular coxosternite, tergites, single claw on last leg, male 14th leg.
Distribution:	A rural species, typically found in woodland or scrub. Southeast England with isolated records from elsewhere (Lancashire, Cheshire).

Lithobius peregrinus

Maximum length:	24 mm.
Colour:	Chestnut brown.
Head:	Broader than long, about as broad as T1 or broader.
Antennae:	Two fifths to one half body length, 38-52 articles.
Ocelli:	11-19 in 3 or 4 curved rows in front of the posterior one.
Forcipular coxosternite:	5 + 5 (5 + 4 to 8 + 7) teeth, frequently of unequal size and spacing.
Tergites:	Posterior projections of T9 triangular, those of T11 and T13 very narrow and prominent.
Coxal pores:	Circular to oval in small specimens, oblong or keyhole shaped in larger, 6 to 8 on each coxa.
Legs:	Coxolateral spines (VaC) present on legs 14 and 15, sometimes 13. Claw of last leg double.
Males:	No conspicuous specific secondary sexual characteristics.
Female genitalia:	Two spurs on each side, claw with both medial and lateral denticles distinct.
Diagnostic features:	Forcipular coxosternite, tergites, coxolateral spines on both legs 14 and 15, female gonopod spurs two (contrasts with *L. piceus*), claw of last leg. Superficial resemblance to *L. forficatus*.
Distribution:	Town centre of Sheerness, Kent, apparently replacing *L. forficatus*. (The only known North European site but possibly now extinct in that locality.)

Lithobius piceus

Maximum length:	21 mm.
Colour:	Chestnut brown.
Head:	A little broader than long, broader than T3 but narrower than T5.
Antennae:	About half body length, 49-54 articles.
Ocelli:	11-16, posterior much larger than others which are arranged in 3-4 fairly straight rows.
Forcipular coxosternite:	3-5 teeth, commonly 4 on each side. Immatures may have as few as 2.
Tergites:	Projections on T9, T11, T13.
Coxal pores:	Round or slightly oval, 4-6 on each side.
Legs:	Coxolateral spine (VaC) on coxa of 15th leg, claw of that leg double.
Males:	No specific secondary sexual characteristics.
Female genitalia:	3-4 conical spurs on each side, claw distinctly bifid in British specimens.
Diagnostic features:	Forcipular coxosternite, tergites, claw of last leg, 15VaC, female gonopod spurs. Superficially resembles *L. forficatus* but even in the field the antennae look longer. In *L. peregrinus*, VaC also occurs on leg 14 and the forcipular coxosternite is different.
Distribution:	Seems to be confined to Surrey, Sussex and Hampshire, mostly in woodland.

Also known as *L. quadridentatus*.

Lithobius pilicornis

Maximum length:	35 mm, our largest lithobiid.
Colour:	Chestnut brown to dark brown.
Head:	As broad as long or a little broader, broader than T5 but narrower than T8.
Antennae:	Two fifths to almost half body length, 29-34 articles.
Ocelli:	20-40, posterior larger than others which are arranged in irregular rows.
Forcipular coxosternite:	3 + 4 to 5 + 6 teeth, slopes gradually back laterally without shoulders.
Tergites:	Posterior angles of T9 right angled, T11 with broad rather blunt projections, T13 with more prominent projections.
Coxal pores:	Oval, slit or dumb-bell shaped, 5-9 on each coxa.
Legs:	The 15th legs are comparatively long and fairly distinctive in the field (almost half body length); they bear single claws. Spine 15VaC is present and also VmC which is not seen on any other British species.
Males:	No specific secondary sexual characteristics.

Female genitalia:	Two conical spurs on each gonopod, well developed dorsal and smaller ventral denticles on claw.
Diagnostic features:	Tergites, forcipular coxosternite, claw of last leg, spines VaC and VmC.
Distribution:	Widespread in SW Devon and parts of Cornwall where it may replace *L. forficatus* in some sites, scattered records from urban sites along the south coast and as far north as Wakefield. Has been recorded indoors. South Wales (Pembrokeshire, etc.), Channel Islands.

Lithobius tenebrosus

Maximum length:	14 mm.
Colour:	Chestnut brown.
Head:	Almost as long as broad.
Antennae:	36-43 articles.
Ocelli:	14-18 in 4 or 5 rows.
Forcipular coxosternite:	2 + 2 teeth in almost a straight line and weakly developed shoulders.
Tergites:	T9, T11 and T13 with small posterior projections, those on T13 not being much larger than those on T9 (unlike *L. melanops*).
Coxal pores:	Round, 3-6 on each coxa.
Legs:	15th leg with single claw.
Males:	No clear specific secondary sexual characteristics.
Female genitalia:	2 conical spurs on each side, claw with dorsal and ventral denticles.
Diagnostic features:	Somewhat resembles *L. melanops* but has only single claw to last leg.
Distribution:	There are older records of this species from Durham and Cornwall and a single modern one of a male (9.5 mm) from Aberystwyth, Mid Wales.

Lithobius tricuspis

Maximum length:	14 mm.
Colour:	Brown with head dark brown.
Head:	A little broader than long, about as broad as T3.
Antennae:	About half body length, 40-45 articles.
Ocelli:	10-12, posterior much larger than others which are arranged in three fairly straight rows.
Forcipular coxosternite:	2 + 2 well developed teeth but without well developed shoulders laterally.
Tergites:	Projections on T9, T11, T13, those on T9 being somewhat broader than the others.

Coxal pores:	Round, 3-4 on each coxa.
Legs:	15 VaC present or absent, claw of 15th leg double. Some continental specimens have only one claw.
Males:	No specific secondary sexual characteristics.
Female genitalia:	3 + 3 somewhat spinous spurs, the internal being rather smaller than the others.
Diagnostic features:	Female gonopod spurs are clearest, 15VaC (if present). Separation from *L. melanops* on shape of forcipular coxosternite, shape of tergites, etc. Generally a much darker animal.
Distribution:	Widespread in village and rural sites in parts of South Devon. Single, isolated records from South Wales and Isle of Wight.

Lithobius variegatus (Plate 12, p. 95)

Maximum length:	24 mm (up to 30 mm in some Irish specimens).
Colour:	Head and tergites pale brown, marbled with dark violet. Underside (including forcipules) yellow, legs marked with alternate pale and dark bands. These colours, which make the animal unmistakable in life fade in preserved specimens.
Head:	About as broad as long or a little broader, much broader than T3, sometimes as broad as T8.
Antennae:	About half body length, 35-46 articles.
Ocelli:	13-18, posterior barely larger than any other. Others arranged in 4 or 5 curved, rather irregular rows.
Forcipular coxosternite:	6 + 6 to 7 +7 teeth on a very prominent anterior border. Sloping sharply backwards without shoulders.
Tergites:	T7 has feeble but distinct posterior projections, the only British species with these. Also projections on T9, T11 and T13.
Coxal pores:	Round (feebly oval in largest specimens), 4-7 (-8) on each coxa.
Legs:	Conspicuously variegated in life. Claw of 15th leg single (very rarely a small accessory claw).
Males:	No specific secondary sexual characteristics.
Female genitalia:	Two broad and rather spatulate spurs on each side, claw with small but distinct ventral denticle and vestigial dorsal.
Diagnostic features:	Colour in life and its habit of remaining motionless initially when disturbed unlike most other species, presumably relying on camouflage. Forcipular coxosternite appearance, T7.
Distribution:	Mostly in village and rural areas in woodland and other sites. Very characteristic of moorland in many areas. Often very common and easily found. All over western Britain but seemingly absent from some eastern counties and much of Scotland. Widespread in Ireland. Channel Islands.

Species of doubtful status in the British Isles

Lithobius agilis

Maximum length:	12 mm.
Antennae:	31-35 articles.
Ocelli:	7-11.
Forcipular coxosternite:	2 + 2 teeth, traces of lateral shoulders.
Tergites:	Broad, blunt projections on T9, more prominent on T11 and T13.
Legs:	15VaC present, claw of last leg double.
Female genitalia:	Two spurs on each gonopod (*L. tricuspis* has 3).
Diagnostic features:	May be difficult to distinguish from *L. tricuspis*.
Distribution:	Old records from Armagh and Donegal and (unpublished) Cornwall. Possibly these were *L. tricuspis* or some other species. Widespread in Europe.

Lithobius erythrocephalus

Maximum length:	16 mm.
Antennae:	28-33 articles.
Ocelli:	10-14.
Forcipular coxosternite:	2 + 2 blunt teeth, barely a trace of shoulders.
Tergites:	T9 and T11 right angled, T11 right angled or with short, blunt projections.
Legs:	15VaC present, claw of last leg double.
Female genitalia:	Two long slender spurs, sometimes a third, claw trifid.
Diagnostic features:	Forcipular coxosternite shape, tergites, 15VaC, female gonopod spurs.
Distribution:	Old records from Northumberland, Ceredigion, Midlothian. Widespread in Europe; could be found in Britain.

SCUTIGEROMORPHA

There is only one member of this group recorded from Britain and it is very unlikely to be confused with any other of our species (Fig. 147). Possibly other species could come in with imported goods.

Scutigera coleoptrata (the house centipede) (Plate 16, p. 96)

Maximum size:	30 mm long body but legs extend widely.
Colour:	Dull violet with 3 longitudinal dorsal violet bands on trunk and violet bands on legs.
Head:	Head capsule almost cubical, not flattened.
Antennae:	Two basal articles (scape) and a long flagellum with up to 500 annuli ('segments') (Fig. 148).
Ocelli:	Compound eyes resembling those of insects on either side of head.
Forcipules:	Coxites separate, three or four long spines on anterior border (Fig. 149).
Trunk:	Stout, not flattened, only seven tergites visible, each with a median posterior notch and a slit-shaped stigma from which lead tracheae.

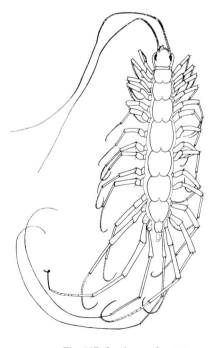

Fig. 147. *Scutigera coleoptrata.*

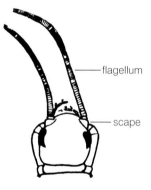

Fig. 148. An enlargement of the head to show the bases of the antennae.

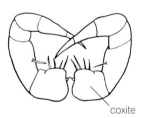

Fig. 149. Forcipules in ventral view.

Legs:

Very elongate, tarsus and metatarsus each divided into numerous elements (Fig. 150). The tarsus-metatarsus of the last legs has 500-600 annulations.

Juveniles:

Newly hatched animals have only 4 leg pairs. These increase with each moult until 15 is reached; there are then several post-larval stages.

Diagnostic features:

Cannot be confused with any other British centipede. Its rapid movement and long legs may cause it to be mistaken for some strange spider-like animal by those unfamiliar with it.

Distribution:

A species typically and sporadically found indoors in Britain. Old records are from as far north as Aberdeen. In recent years it has been found in Devon, Dorset, Hampshire, Kent, Lancashire, London, Hampshire, Suffolk and Wiltshire. It seems to be well established in buildings in the Channel Islands and has been found outdoors in Jersey.

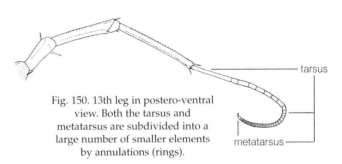

Fig. 150. 13th leg in postero-ventral view. Both the tarsus and metatarsus are subdivided into a large number of smaller elements by annulations (rings).

GLOSSARY

Accessory claw. Claw(s) in addition to the main one on legs e.g. of lithobiomorphs making the claw double (or triple) instead of single. The one on the 15th leg may be important in identification (Fig. 103).

Accessory spine. A spine in addition to the normal three seen on the prefemur of the last legs of *Lithobius borealis* (Fig. 138).

Annulations, annuli. Rings round some articles of legs and/or antennae giving the appearance that they are subdivided into many smaller articles (Figs 148, 150).

Articles. The 'segments' of appendages (antennae, legs (Fig. 5), mouthparts). Strictly the word segment should be used for segments of the body.

Basal node (Basal tooth). A tooth-like projection found at the base of the poison claw in many geophilomorphs.

Carpophagus structure. An arrangement seen on certain sequential sternites in geophilomorphs where there is a posterior peg from one sternite and a matching anterior pit (fossa) on the anterior part of the one behind (Fig. 63).

Clearing. A process using Hoyers' mountant, 50% lactic acid or ethylene glycol to render the animal rather transparent and thus, hopefully, show up certain structures.

Clypeus. The anterior, ventral portion of the head capsule bearing the labrum posteriorly (Fig. 4).

Combs. On the tibia (tibial comb, Fig. 91) and tarsus (tarsal comb, Fig. 92) of the last legs of *Cryptops* are a row of tooth-like structures sometimes called 'saw teeth'.

Compound eye. An eye made up of a group of closely grouped units each with its lens as in insects and *Scutigera*.

Concavity of poison claw. The inner edge of the claw (Fig. 71). This may be smooth or crenulate i.e. with a series of teeth or incisions.

Coxa (pl.coxae). The most basal part of the leg, attaching it to the pleurites (Fig. 5).

Coxal pores. Openings of glands in the coxae of the legs. In geophilomorphs these are on the last pair of legs (Fig. 25), on lithobiomorphs the last four pairs (Fig. 112) and on *Cryptops* they form the cribriform area on the last pair of legs (Fig. 80).

Coxites. A term used for the basal parts of the forcipules as in *Scutigera* (Fig. 149) (see also coxosternite).

Coxolateral spine. A term sometimes used for the spine 15VaC in *Lithobius*; of systematic value (Fig. 107).

Coxosternite. The bases of the forcipules fused to the sternite as seen, for instance in *Lithobius* (Fig. 96) or *Cryptops* (Fig. 89).

Cribriform area. The area of pores on the coxae of the last legs of *Cryptops* (Fig. 80).

Cruciform suture. A diagonal cross like groove on T1 of *Cryptops anomalans* (Fig. 74).

Denticle – the gonopod claw of lithobiids may have accessory 'teeth' on either side of the claw making it appear double or triple.

Femur. One of the articles of the leg, between the prefemur and the tibia (Fig. 5).

Forcipular coxosternite. The large basal structure formed from fused coxae and sternites at the base of the forcipules (Fig. 2).

Forcipular coxosternite teeth. Teeth on the anterior margin of the forcipular coxosternite between the claws and seen in lithobiomorphs (Fig. 140) and in *Scolopendra* spp.

Forcipular segment. The body segment bearing the forcipules (with poison claws).

Forcipular tergite. The dorsal plate (tergite) of the forcipular segment. In *Cryptops* it is fused with the first trunk tergite and referred to as T1.

Forcipules. The modified first pair of legs bearing the poison claws which lie under the posterior part of the head (Fig. 2).

Fossa (pl.fossae). Pits or depressions especially on the sternites.

Gonopod. Limb modified for reproductive purposes seen ventrally on the terminal segments. In male geophilomorphs a pair of gonopods are visible (Fig. 11) but females show only a pair of anal valves (Fig. 12). In lithobiomorphs the female gonopods are very obvious and bear spurs and claws (Fig. 114) making sexing of these animals straightforward.

Gonopod claw. In female lithobiomorphs the gonopod bears a claw which may have a characteristic appearance because of the one or two lateral denticles (teeth) it has (Fig. 108).

Gonopod spurs. In female lithobiomorphs there are two or more conical or spinous spurs on the base of the gonopod (Fig. 108). In immature females they are less well developed. Three spurs on each gonopod are characteristic of *Lithobius tricuspis* and 3 or 4 of *Lithobius piceus*. Other species may occasionally have 3 on one or both sides.

Instar. During development, centipedes undergo a series of moults (ecdyses); the period between each moult is referred to as an instar (or stadium), the final stage being the adult or maturus stage.

Labrum. At the posterior border of the clypeus and in front of the mouthparts; it may have characteristic spines, teeth or other structures (Fig. 4).

Larval stages. In lithobiomorphs and scutigeromorphs where the animal hatches with less than the adult number of legs, the series of instars during which successive leg pairs are added are referred to as larval. Those with 15 leg pairs before the adult stage is reached are the post-larval instars.

Mandibles. The first pair of mouthparts, 'biting' structures homologous with the same structures in insects (Fig. 4).

Maxillae. 1st and 2nd maxillae are the second and third pairs of mouthparts. The claws of the latter may be of systematic importance in some geophilomorphs (Fig. 3).

Metasternite. Sternites may be divided into an anterior presternite and a posterior metasternite. In the case of a description of the arrangement of the coxal pores on the last legs of geophilomorphs, the metasternite is the metasternite of the last trunk segment, the rather trapezoidal plate between the two coxae (Fig. 15).

Metatarsus. The last leg article before the claw where the tarsus is divided into two parts (see Tarsus).

Ocelli. Simple eyes, seen in lithobiomorphs; in *Scutigera* the eyes are close together in a compound eye resembling that of insects (Fig. 125). Absent in *Cryptops* and in geophilomorphs.

Paradontal spine. A spine lateral to the teeth on the forcipular coxosternite of *Lithobius*.

Pharynx. The beginning of the digestive system.

Pleurites. The lateral plates on each segment (Fig. 5).

Poison claw. (In this context) the actual claw of the forcipules (Fig. 2).

Prefemur. Article of leg between the short trochanter and the femur (Fig. 5).

Presternite – see sternite.

Saw teeth. The combs of teeth on the tibia and tarsus of *Cryptops* species.

Scape. In *Scutigera* each antenna has a more solid basal region of two articles known as the scape and an elongate, multi-ringed, whip-like flagellum (Fig. 148).

Sclerites. Chitinous plates that make up the exoskeleton (tergites, sternites, etc.).

Seta (pl.setae). A bristle or hair-like structures, not to be confused with the more stout spines of *Lithobius* species which have both setae and spines.

Spines. In *Lithobius* these are rather stout structures with a well-defined base (which should be visible even if the spine has broken off) seen on the coxa, trochanter, prefemur, femur, tibia and tarsus of legs. They are of systematic importance (Figs 98, 99).

Spinulation. The arrangement of spines on the legs in *Lithobius*. Specific spines such as VaC as well as the extent of particular spine series are of taxonomic importance (Figs 98, 99). The formula for spinulation comprises D (dorsal) or V (ventral side); anterior (a), median (m) or posterior (p); coxa (C), trochanter (t), prefemur (p), femur (F) or tibia (T). Legs are numbered 1-15 from the head. Generally spine m is larger than a or p.

Stadium. Instar.

Sternal pores. Openings of numbers of small glands in the sternite. In *Geophilus*, for example, they are concentrated in a small area of the metasternite just anterior to the carpophagus peg. Their occurrence and appearance may be of systematic importance.

Sternites. The ventral plates of the body segments. They may be divided into an anterior presternite and a larger, posterior metasternite. Sternites may bear pores or other structures.

Sulcus (pl.sulci). A furrow or groove.

Suture. A seam or line indicating where two sclerites are immovably connected.

Synanthropic sites. Those seriously influenced by human activity e.g. gardens, urban sites, etc.

S1, S2, etc. The sternites of the trunk (sternite 1, etc.).

Tarsal comb. An arrangement of teeth seen on the ventral margin of the tarsus of the last legs of *Cryptops* species (Fig. 84).

Tarsus. A leg article, between the tibia and metatarsus (Fig. 5). In certain lithobiids the tarsus and metatarsus may be fused to form a single structure.

Telopodite. The term used to denote the segments of the leg after the coxa. Also applicable to the forcipules.

Tergite. The dorsal plates seen on the forcipular segment, trunk segments and terminal segments.

Terminal segments. The last segments of the body beyond those bearing legs.

Tibia. A leg article, between the femur and tarsus (Fig. 5).

Tibial comb. An arrangement of teeth seen on the ventral margin of the tibia of the last legs of *Cryptops* species (Fig. 83). Note that there is no trochanter in these legs so that it is the third article after the coxa.

Tömösváry, organ of. A sensory pit just anterior and ventral to the ocelli in Lithobiomorpha (shown as a pale dot below the ocelli in Fig. 118). It may look somewhat like an ocellus in *Lithobius* and needs to be distinguished.

Transition. A region of the trunk of many geophilomorphs where there is a more or less well defined change in appearance of the segments (Fig. 22).

Trochanter. The small leg article between the coxa and the prefemur (Fig. 5). Absent in *Cryptops*.

Trunk. The leg-bearing segments of the body, behind the head.

Tubercle. A small swollen structure, not to be confused with a claw at the apex of the last legs of some species.

T1, T7, etc. The various tergites of the trunk region (tergite 1, tergite 7, etc.).

VaC. A small coxolateral spine seen on the 15th coxa of some species of *Lithobius*; of systematic importance (Fig. 107).

VmC. A relatively conspicuous spine behind the coxal pores on the 15th leg of *Lithobius pilicornis* (Fig. 107).

Virguliform fossae. Small comma-shaped lateral fossae (pits) on certain sternites of *Stigmatogaster subterranea*.

BIBLIOGRAPHY

Arthur, W., Foddai,D., Kettle, C., Lewis, J.G.E., Luczynski, M, Minelli, A. (2001) Analysis of segment number and enzyme variation in a centipede reveals a cryptic species, *Geophilus easoni* sp.nov., and raises questions about speciation. *Biol. J. Linn. Soc.* **74**, 489-499.

Barber, A.D. (1992) *Lithobius lapidicola* Meinert, 1872 in Britain. *Bull. Br. Myriapod Group* **8**, 25-30.

Barber, A.D. (1995) *Lithobius lucifugus* L.Koch (Chilopoda, Lithobiomorpha), a centipede new to the British Isles from Scotland. *Bull. Br. Myriapod Group* **11**, 63-65.

Barber A.D. & Eason, E.H. (1970) On *Brachyschendyla dentata* Brolemann & Ribaut (Chilopoda, Schendylidae), a centipede new to Britain. *J. nat. Hist.*, **4**, 79-84.

Barber, A.D. & Eason, E.H., (1986) A redescription of *Lithobus peregrinus* Latzel (Chilopoda, Lithobiomorpha), a centipede new to Britain. *J. nat. Hist.*, **20**, 431-437.

Barber, A.D. & Keay, A.N. (1988) *Provisional Atlas of the Centipedes of the British Isles*, NERC, Huntingdon.

Blower, J.G. (1985) *Millipedes*. Synopses of the British Fauna No. 35. Brill, London.

Brölemann, H.W. (1930) *Éléments d'une Faune des Myriapodes de France*, Chilopodes, Imprimerie Toulousaine. Reprinted 1970 by Kraus.

Chilobase. http://chilobase.bio.unipd.it/search

Demange, J-M. (1981) *Les Mille-pattes*, Editions Boubée, Paris.

Eason, E.H. (1964) *Centipedes of the British Isles*, Warne, London.

Eason, E.H., (1965) On *Lithobius tricuspis* Meinert (Chilopoda, Lithobiidae) in Britain. *Ann. Mag. nat. Hist (13)*, **8**, 285-292.

Jones, R.E., (1989) On a new species of centipede (Chilopoda, Geophilomorpha) from the Isles of Scilly. *J. nat. Hist.*, **23**, 627-633 (*Arenophilus peregrinus*).

Jones, R.E. & Barber, A.D., (1997) A description of *Chalandea pinguis* (Brölemann, 1898). *Bull. Br. Myriapod Group* **13**, 22-26.

Keay, A.N. (1989) *Lithobius tenebrosus* Meinert from Aberystwyth, Cardiganshire. *Bull. Br. Myriapod Group* **6**, 3-5.

Lewis, J.G.E. (1981) *The Biology of Centipedes*, Cambridge University Press, Cambridge. (Reissued 2007.)

Lewis, J.G.E. (2007) On *Cryptops doriae* Pocock, from the wet tropical biome of the Eden project, Cornwall (Chilopoda, Scolopendromorpha, Cryptopsidae) *Bull. Brit. Myriapod Isopod Group* **22**, 12-16.

Lewis, J.G.E., Jones, R.E., & Keay, A.N., (1988) On a new species of centipede (Chilopoda, Geophilomorpha, Chilenophilidae) from the British Isles. *J. nat. Hist.*, **22**, 1657-1663 (*Nothogeophilus turki*)

Lewis, J.G.E. & Rundle, A.J. (1988) *Tygarrup javanicus* (Attems) a geophilomorph centipede new to the British Isles. *Bull. Br. Myriapod Group* **5**, 3-5

Pereira, L.A. (2000) The preparation of centipedes for microscopical examination with particular reference to the Geophilomorpha. *Bull. Br. Myriapod Group* **16**, 22-25.

Richards, P. (1995) *Millipedes, Centipedes and Woodlice of the Sheffield Area*, Sorby Natural History Society, Sheffield Museum.

Tilling, S.M. (1987) A key to the major groups of British terrestrial invertebrates. *Field Studies* **6**, 695-766.

Index

The start of main entries are shown in **bold**, plates in *italic*. Synonyms are given in *italic*.

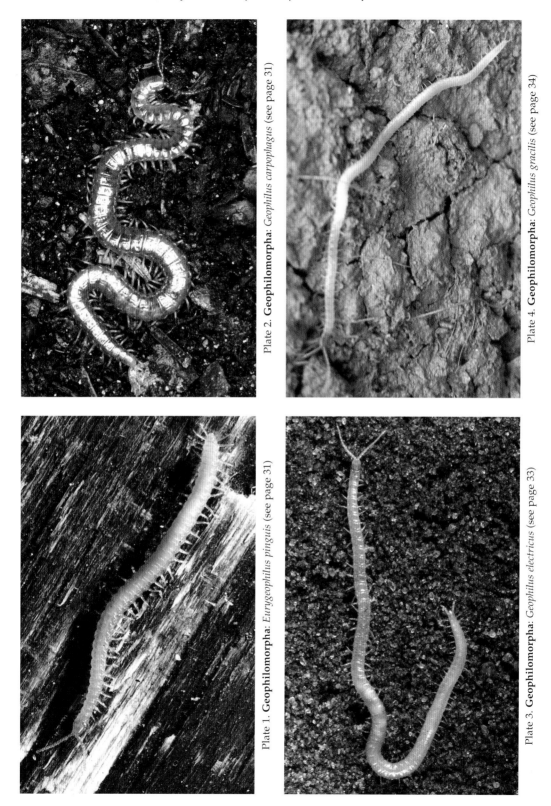

Plate 2. **Geophilomorpha**: *Geophilus carpophagus* (see page 31)

Plate 4. **Geophilomorpha**: *Geophilus gracilis* (see page 34)

Plate 1. **Geophilomorpha**: *Eurygeophilus pinguis* (see page 31)

Plate 3. **Geophilomorpha**: *Geophilus electricus* (see page 33)

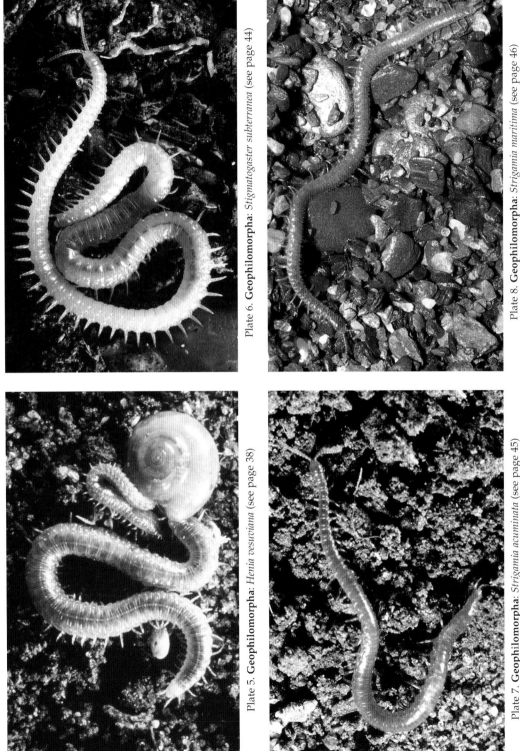

Plate 6. **Geophilomorpha:** *Stigmatogaster subterranea* (see page 44)

Plate 8. **Geophilomorpha:** *Strigamia maritima* (see page 46)

Plate 5. **Geophilomorpha:** *Henia vesuviana* (see page 38)

Plate 7. **Geophilomorpha:** *Strigamia acuminata* (see page 45)

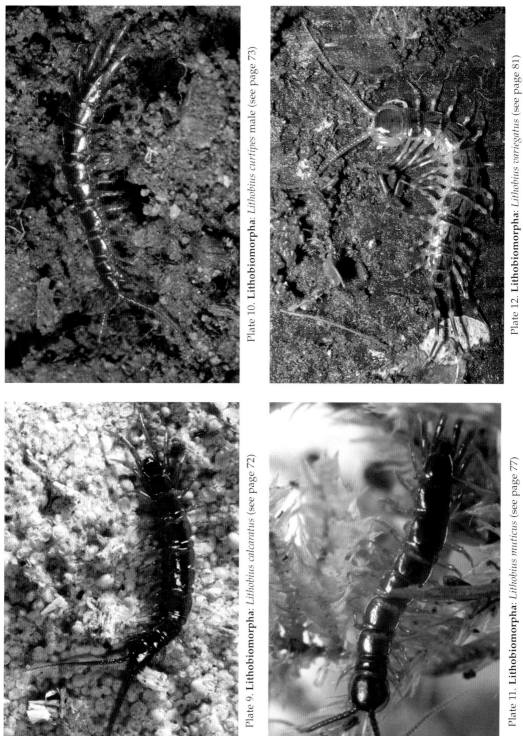

Plate 10. **Lithobiomorpha:** *Lithobius curtipes* male (see page 73)

Plate 12. **Lithobiomorpha:** *Lithobius variegatus* (see page 81)

Plate 9. **Lithobiomorpha:** *Lithobius calcaratus* (see page 72)

Plate 11. **Lithobiomorpha:** *Lithobius muticus* (see page 77)

Plate 14. **Scolopenromorpha**: *Cryptops hortensis* (see page 53)

Plate 16. **Scutigeomorpha**: *Scutigera coleoptrata* (see page 83)

Plate 13. **Scolopenromorpha**: *Cryptops anomalans* (see page 52)

Plate 15. **Scolopenromorpha**: *Cryptops parsi – head* (see page 54)